# Inter-professional approaches
# to young fathers

# Other Health & Social Care books from M&K

Books can be ordered online at: www.mkupdate.co.uk

Pre-Teen and Teenage Pregnancy:
A 21st century reality
ISBN: 978-1-905539-11-6 · 2007

Routine Blood Results Explained 2/e
ISBN: 978-1-905539-38-3 · 2007

The Management of COPD in Primary and Secondary Care
ISBN: 978-1-905539-28-4 · 2007

The Clinician's Guide to Chronic Disease Management
for Long Term Conditions:
A cognitive-behavioural approach
ISBN: 978-1-905539-15-4 · 2008

Identification and Treatment of Alcohol Dependency
ISBN: 978-1-905539-16-1 · Forthcoming 2008

Managing Emotions in Women's Health
ISBN: 978-1-905539-07-9 · Forthcoming 2008

Living with Dying:
Perspectives on death, dying and living with loss
ISBN: 978-1-905539-21-5 · Forthcoming 2008

# Inter-professional approaches to young fathers

Edited by Jane Reeves

Inter-professional approaches to young fathers
Jane Reeves

ISBN: 978-1-905539-29-1

First published 2008

**British Library Catalogue in Publication Data**
A catalogue record for this book is available from the British Library

Notice
Clinical practice and medical knowledge constantly evolve. Standard safety precautions must be followed, but, as knowledge is broadened by research, changes in practice, treatment and drug therapy may become necessary or appropriate. Readers must check the most current product information provided by the manufacturer of each drug to be administered and verify the dosages and correct administration, as well as contraindications. It is the responsibility of the practitioner, utilising the experience and knowledge of the patient, to determine dosages and the best treatment for each individual patient. Any brands mentioned in this book are as examples only and are not endorsed by the Publisher. Neither the publisher nor the authors assume any liability for any injury and/or damage to persons or property arising from this publication.

*The Publisher*

To contact M&K Publishing write to:
M&K Update Ltd · The Old Bakery · St. John's Street
Keswick · Cumbria CA12 5AS

Tel: 01768 773030 · Fax: 01768 781099
publishing@mkupdate.co.uk
www.mkupdate.co.uk

Designed and typeset in 11 pt Usherwood by Mary Blood
Printed in England by Ferguson Print, Keswick

# Contents

# Figures

# Tables

# Contributors

**Ros Delaney, Senior Lecturer, RGN, RM, ADM, PGCEA, BSc. (Hons),** Senior Lecturer Sexual Health, Department of Family Care and Mental Health, School of Health and Social Care, University of Greenwich.

**Liz Gale, RGN, RM, BSc. (Hons),** Senior Lecturer Midwifery, Department of Family Care and Mental Health, School of Health and Social Care, University of Greenwich.

**Rosa Panades-Blas BA (Hons) Sociology, MA Social Research,** Full Time PhD Student, Department of Family Care and Mental Health, School of Health and Social Care, University of Greenwich.

**Dr Jane Reeves, BA (Hons), CQSW, MPhil, PhD,** Research Lead, Department of Family Care and Mental Health, School of Health and Social Care, University of Greenwich.

**Frances Rehal RN RHV, BSc,** Chief Executive, Sure Start Millmead.

**Janet Webb RN Child, RGN, RNT, MSc Research (Health), BEd, Diploma in Nursing,** Professional Lead Child Health and Welfare, Department of Family Care and Mental Health, School of Health and Social Care, University of Greenwich.

For our children: Richard, Charlotte, Isabelle, Wills, Henry, Alice, Samuel, Sorcha, Liam, Sergio and Nico.

# Introduction

**Jane Reeves**

> With one of the highest teenage pregnancy rates in Europe, young fatherhood, as a site of economic and personal adversity, has become a focus of concern in Britain during the late 1990s. However, despite this policy interest there is surprisingly little British empirical evidence to review.
>
> (O'Brian 2004: 20)

Research interest in young fathers has grown from the large amount of contemporary literature on teenage mothers (SEU 1999, 2004, Swann *et al.* 2003) as well as raised awareness of fatherhood generally (Tyrer *et al.* 2005). Like O'Brian (2004), quoted above, the Teenage Pregnancy Unit (SEU 1999, 2004) argues that fathers are still a largely unexplored part of the 'problem' of teenage pregnancy, although some studies in the UK have looked at their contribution (Simms & Smith 1986, Hudson & Ineichen 1991, Speak *et al.* 1997, Tyrer *et al.* 2005, Reeves 2006). Most of the policy initiatives on teenage pregnancy have been aimed at mothers and their children, however a recent document argued that 'while the negative consequences of teenage pregnancy are felt most by young women and their children, it is important that strategies to reduce teenage pregnancy also impact on young men's attitudes and behaviour' (DfES 2006: 7).

Generally however, the needs of young fathers in the UK have gone largely unnoticed and there is great variation, and thus no consistency, amongst regions in the UK in terms of how much work is done with them (Sheriff 2007).

Recent figures indicate that there are some 80,000 registered married and unmarried young fathers under the age of 24 (www.statistics.gov.uk/2005), a substantial number, and many may benefit from professional help. However, these statistics on young fathers in the UK, whilst providing some insight, do not reveal the full extent of young men who father a child, as the figures only include those who are named on the child's birth certificate. Moreover, these statistics also do not include ethnic background or whether a young father is resident or non-resident in their child's life.

If, in line with the statistics above, 24 and under is taken as the 'benchmark' for considering young fathers, it can be seen that research which directly focuses on the needs of this group is in its infancy. Indeed, it is widely agreed that young fathers do not form a homogeneous group: some young fathers are resident, some are not and this status may change over time, some may be offenders, some may have a physical or learning disability and others may have varied cultural and ethnic influences on them. It is, however, possible to identify factors which make some young men vulnerable to becoming a father at a young age and these factors are primarily linked to deprivation and social exclusion. Young fathers are more likely to come from lower socio-economic groups (Hudson & Ineichen 1991, Swann et al. 2003) and families facing financial hardships (Kiernan 1995; Tyrer et al. 2005). In addition, they are likely to have left school at the minimum age and as Tyrer et al. (2005: 1108) remark they, 'are more likely to have engaged in youth offending, with some estimates suggesting that more than a quarter of young men in young offenders institutions are already fathers or expectant fathers.' Moreover, teenage relationships are also fragile and in danger of breaking down (Allen & Dowling 1998) with recent research from the US indicating that multi-partnering is becoming increasingly common with either party moving on to further relationships and to have more children (Benjamin & Furstenberg 2007; Raneri & Weinmann 2007) creating a web of often complex young families, with which professionals are increasingly involved. Accordingly, a young man could be a biological father to children he is living with and some that he is not and he may also be living with children that are not his own, further complicating his life and relationships. This book is primarily concerned with resident and non-resident young fathers and their biological children, although some of the scenarios and practice points in the book could be applied to young men and their cohabiting children.

It is pointed out that 'data on young fathers is less easy to come by because it is not systematically collated' (Swann *et al.* 2003: 13) but also because young fathers, particularly if they are non-resident, are a difficult group to gain access to (Tyrer *et al.* 2005; Reeves 2006). It would seem that there are many divergent reasons for this, for example as Daniel and Taylor (2001, 2003) point out in their work on fathers generally, current services which intervene with vulnerable families are often maternally focused and this can lead to paternal views being ignored. Moreover, where they are contacted by professionals, young fathers can be difficult to reach, perhaps due to transitory lifestyles, and also they may be suspicious or fearful about participating (Reeves 2006). Consequently, many studies incorporate the 'views' of young fathers through the thoughts, feelings and opinions of young mothers (Corlyon & McGuire 1997; Reeves 2003) and their direct opinions are under-represented.

## The basis of the book

There is, therefore, for a variety of reasons a lack of evidence which focuses on the direct views of young men who become fathers and how their needs can be met. This book is intended for individuals and professionals (sexual health workers, midwives, nurses, health visitors, social workers) involved in the lives of resident and non-resident young fathers and those studying or working with them. Consequently, the purpose of this book, drawing on policy, literature, research evidence and theoretical perspectives, is to consider the often 'hidden' aspect of teenage pregnancy, the standpoint of the young father, from the time he becomes sexually active and possibly fathering a child through to his attachment with his child or children. Each chapter makes use of 'good practice' boxes. The purpose of these boxes is for students and practitioners to consider pertinent professional issues and each box highlights topics for debate and good practice. There are also significant themes which run through each chapter, either explicitly or implicitly, including social exclusion, risk, complexity, vulnerability, responsibility and resilience.

One of the aims of the book is to draw together contemporary research evidence, social theory and policy which may effect how practitioners, students and academics conceptualise and work with young fathers. Consequently, each chapter illustrates the points it makes using discrete evidence from that particular field. Moreover, in order to make this process more 'user friendly' each chapter provides a summary of this literature and evidence. Finally, in order to make the book come alive the book draws on case studies which are drawn, variously, from two studies conducted by the editor.

● Study 1 draws on material from an MPhil study of 24 white mothers in the care system (Reeves 2003) where the young women were specifically asked about their partners.

● Study 2 draws on material from a PhD study of 16 white young fathers aged between 16 and 24, conducted in the UK (Reeves 2006) using narrative interviews.

Whilst it is acknowledged that there are limitations to these studies, based upon relatively small numbers and the reliance on white participants, the case scenarios they provide are useful points of reference to facilitate discussion. Many of the chapters use the same case studies, emphasising the point that working with young fathers is a multi-professional responsibility.

## How the book is organised

**Chapter 1**, by Jane Reeves and Frances Rehal, is introductory and identifies the underpinning issues in relation to young fathers, including thinking about young relationships, family support networks and professional relationships. The innovations in practice put forward by Sure Start are also considered in relation to engaging and working with young vulnerable parents. The key issues are contextualised and related to the wider discussions in each of the ensuing chapters.

**Chapter 2**, by Jan Webb, considers the contemporary arena of policy and law which shapes the way practitioners think about and work with young families generally and young fathers specif-ically. The chapter sets out key parts of the Children Act 1989, 2004, Every Child Matters, and The Human Rights Act 1998, and contemplates the possible tensions inherent for professionals in working with young fathers, who may still be legally children themselves, and their offspring.

**Chapter 3**, by Ros Delaney moves on to look at sexual health issues for young men, particularly in terms of setting up and encouraging the use of sexual health services by young men. The chapter covers legal, moral and theoretical approaches to working with young men and suggests practical ways of engaging with them and encouraging safe sexual practices.

Moving forward to the discovery of the pregnancy, Liz Gale, in **Chapter 4** focuses on the interaction of health professionals with young fathers through the ante-natal to post-natal periods. The chapter considers initial reactions to the pregnancy by the young father and how midwives in particular can pave the way to positive future relationships by health professionals generally with young men. It discusses the role of the midwife with young fathers at antenatal appointments and how to actively engage with them during labour and in the weeks beyond the birth.

In **Chapter 5** we return to Jan Webb who this time focuses specifically on safeguarding young fathers and their children. The chapter considers in detail the principles which underpin how we think about children and young people and ensure they remain safe. It looks in detail at the terminology that is used when considering young families and how practitioners can work effectively in partnership with young, often vulnerable, families.

In **Chapter 6** Rosa Panades-Blas considers the relationships that young fathers have with their children. She takes a contemporary 'snapshot' of fatherhood in the UK and goes on to consider the characteristics of young fathers and how they engage with their children and how this may vary dependent upon being a resident or non-resident father. She also considers how professionals may view young fathers and looks at underlying theoretical perspectives which inform this. Finally she considers the stresses on young fathers and argues that professionals need to take this into consideration when working with them.

Finally, **Chapter 7**, by Jane Reeves, looks at how, rather than young fatherhood being considered negatively, in some cases becoming a father may be a deterrent factor amongst young men involved within the criminal justice system. In the chapter a small group of young men describe how becoming a father altered their perceptions on life, encouraging them to distance themselves from their antisocial peers and to adopt positions of greater responsibility towards their girlfriends and babies.

## References

Allen, I. & Dowling, S. (1998). *Teenage Mothers: Decisions and Outcomes*. London: Policy Studies Institute.

Benjamin, K. & Furstenberg, F. (2007). 'Multipartnered fertility among young women with a nonmarital first birth: Prevalence and risk factors' in *Perspectives on Sexual and Reproductive Health* 39(1): 29–38.

Corlyon, J. & McGuire, C. (1997). *Young Parents in Public Care*. London: National Children's Bureau.

Daniel, B. & Taylor, J. (2001). *Engaging with Fathers: Practice Issues for Health and Social Care*. London: Jessica Kingsley.

Daniel, B. & Taylor, J. (2003). 'Engaging with fathers: Practice issues for health and social care' in *Child and Family Social Work* 8(1) February: 80–94.

Department for Education and Skills (DfES) (2006). *Teenage Pregnancy Next Steps: Guidance for Local Authorities and Primary Care Trusts on Effective Delivery of Local Strategies*. London: HMSO.

Hudson, F. & Ineichen, B. (1991). *Taking it Lying Down: Sexuality and Teenage Motherhood*. Basingstoke: Macmillan Publishing.

Kiernan, K. (1995). *The Transition to Parenthood: Young Mothers, Young Fathers, Associated Factors and Later Life Experiences*. Discussion Paper 113, London, LSE.

O'Brian, M. (2004). *Fathers and Family Support: Promoting Involvement and Evaluating Impact*. London: National Family and Parenting Institute.

Raneri, L. & Weinmann, C. (2007). 'Social ecological predictors of repeat adolescent pregnancy' in *Sexual and Reproductive Health* 39(1): 39–47.

Reeves, J. (2003). *They Should Still Be Out Playing: A Contemporary Analysis of Young Pregnant Women/Mothers in the Care System*. Unpublished Thesis for Master of Philosophy in Social Work. University of Kent, Canterbury.

Reeves, J. (2006). '*You've got to keep your head on*' A study of the stories young male service users tell about the transition to fatherhood. Unpublished thesis: The Open University.

Sheriff, N. (2007). *Supporting Young Fathers: Examples of Promising Practice*. Brighton: Trust for the Study of Adolescence.

Simms, M. & Smith, C. (1986). *Teenage Mothers and their Partners*. London: HMSO.

Social Exclusion Unit (1999). *Teenage Pregnancy*. London: HMSO.

Social Exclusion Unit (2004). *Impact of the Teenage Pregnancy Strategy: Programme Report*. London: HMSO.
Available at  www.dfes.gov.uk/teenagepregnancy (accessed 2005).

Speak, S., Cameron, S., & Gilroy, R. (1997) 'Young, Single, Non-residential Fathers: Their Involvement in Fatherhood.'
Available at www.jrf.org.uk/knowledge/findings/socialpolicy/sp137.asp

Swann, C., Bowe, K., McCormic, G. & Kosmin, M. (2003). *Teenage Pregnancy and Parenthood: A Review of Reviews: Evidence Briefing*. www.hda.nhs.uk (accessed 2004).

Tyrer, P., Chase, E., Warwick, I. & Aggleton, P. (2005), ' "Dealing with It." Experiences of young fathers in and leaving care' in *British Journal of Social Work* 35: 1107–1121.

www.statistics.gov.uk/2005

# Chapter 1
# Contextualising the evidence: Young fathers, family and professional support
**Jane Reeves and Frances Rehal**

Dear Jude,

We have got ourselves in a bit of trouble but this baby is what I wont more than anything. You no I love you so so much and I would do anythink 4 you. I am trying to cut down on smoking I've only had 1 and its 2.30 so I am trying. But please tell me if you want to get rid of the baby, I would do it 4 you. We will have it for the rest of our lives but we will be together 4 ever any way, won't we. It means so much 2 me when we have sex it ain't just a bit of fun in my eyes. I'm going to have 2 do a test so we know 4 sure but I really do think I am. I will be so upset if I ain't because I want your baby. Please wright back babe.

Love you so
f*****g much,

Tanya

(Reeves 2006: xvi)

## Introduction

As the letter above indicates, teenage parenthood is complex. The purpose of this initial chapter is to contextualise and set out some of the key issues when considering working with or studying young fathers. Little is known about those who provide practical and emotional support for young fathers and this book aims to address this. Accordingly, this chapter will explore positive and negative influences on young fathers and set out features in family members and professionals which young fathers identify as being a hindrance or helpful.

## Young relationships; mutually supportive or 'bang, bang I'm gone' (MacDonald & Marsh 2005)

**Young relationships**

Stereotypical and anecdotal images of teenage relationships often present them as transitory, with the 'blame' often placed on the absence of the young man, with the sound of the door slamming after him (Hudson & Ineichen 1991). Indeed, as the authors surmise 'cupid's arrow does not fly far for teenagers nor is it very robust for its effects do not last' (Hudson & Ineichen 1991: 71). MacDonald and Marsh (2005) in their study, report that popular views of young fathers saw them as 'fearful of adult responsibilities of parenthood' (2005: 139). Other, contradictory evidence, albeit from the perspective of the young woman, suggests that rather than young men leaving when they become fathers:

> More fathers appear to be pushed out than drop out. Young mothers did not want them in their lives with their additional demands, smelly feet and useless offers of help. They had nothing to offer except an increased workload.
>
> (Corlyon & McGuire 1997: 85)

It does appear that representations of young men whose main motivation is to be sexually promiscuous and irresponsible in the face of fatherhood may be more complex. Indeed, as Robb (2007) points out there has been a particular absence of research on the intimacy of young people's lives and specifically what teenage relationships mean for young men. However, as he suggests the current generation of young people are increasingly exposed to the discourse of love and romance by the mass media (Robb 2007) which perpetuates images of romantic love which many young men may not be able to cope with. Indeed, as Firminger (2006) highlights through her analysis of teenage girls' magazines, teenage boys are often presented by two contrasting discourses: on the one hand as shallow, highly sexual, emotionally inexpressive and insecure, but on the other as potential boyfriends who may provide romance, intimacy and love. If a teenage relationship is accelerated by the birth of a baby there may not be time for these two contrasting discourses to be reconciled. We simply do not know enough about the profiles of teenage relationships from the perspectives of young men prior to the birth of a child.

Indeed, in terms of parenting literature generally, it is often reported that the first year of any relationship following the birth of a child is arduous (Oakely 1979). In teenage relationships, however, what we mostly hear about is that young relationships with a child often flounder during the first year (Allen & Dowling 1998; Tabberer *et al.* 2000). Consequently, as professionals considering the needs of young parents and who may be the first professionals with whom these young people have had contact, we have a responsibility to engage with them in a way that is meaningful to them. As Chapter 3 indicates, sexual health services are often meaningless to young men as they often feel the focus is on young women.

## The involvement of fathers in teenage pregnancy

'Part of the problem lies in simply being male.'
(Hudson & Ineichen 1991: 164)

**Involvement of fathers**

It is suggested that the involvement of fathers in teenage pregnancy and beyond is complex, particularly when considering descriptions by young mothers (Reeves 2003).

- In the study of 24 young mothers in the care system, it was found that the older the father the less supportive and more exploitative he was likely to be, for example, openly living with another woman or in another relationship and providing little financial or emotional help.

- This is particularly pertinent as Harner (2004) points out that it is estimated that two-thirds of teenage pregnancies are fathered by adult men. Her study identifies that 'the incidence of domestic violence was twice as great among teenagers with older partners than those partnering with males of a similar age' (Harner 2004: 317). She identifies, in terms of age profile, that the oldest adult males are the fathers of the youngest teenagers' infants, which may have ethical implications for professionals working in sexual health services. The research also points out imbalances in educational and social status as well as economic contributions between older fathers and teenage mothers.

● By comparison, the younger fathers in Reeves' (2003) study who were living with young mothers were more likely to be described in positive terms as contributing to a greater degree financially and emotionally and with the baby.

Bunting and McAuley (2004) also studied the role of fathers and the support they offered to teenage mothers. Analysing social work literature in both the UK and the US they emphasised the intricate and changing landscape of support relationships for young mothers and the specific role of young fathers, biological or cohabiting, in this. They argue that teenage mothers experience significant changes in their social support networks following the birth of a baby. Family support has been indicated as being extremely helpful in ensuring the 'success' of teenage mothers managing their babies. In particular, Tabberer *et al.* (2000) and Allen and Dowling (1998) point out that mothers are vitally important to their teenage daughters prior to and following the birth of a child, often helping in the process of normalising and 'capturing' the pregnancy within existing community and social relationships. Indeed, for some mothers and daughters the pregnancy and birth of a child has been shown to be a 'healing' factor between them, helping them move forward in their relationship (Reeves 2003). As Hudson and Ineichen (1991) remark, 'the most significant person in the pregnant adolescent's life is not always the baby's father; it is usually her mother'. However, support from the young woman's mother has been shown to decrease over time and it is consequently the support from 'partners' which increases in importance. Bunting and McAuley (2004) argue that the presence of a 'man' or 'partner' or 'romantic interest' becomes increasingly important as a mechanism of support, perhaps tying in with recent data from the US which suggests that women who become teenage mothers at a young age are more likely to go on to multi-partner when their initial relationship breaks down (Raneri and Weinmann 2007) as they need continuing support from another adult. In Chapter 6 Rosa Panades-Blas considers the stresses and strains that may exist in teenage relationships for young fathers and the implica-tions this may have on the relationship between the young man and his child and how professionals can recognise these tensions.

---

**Good Practice Box**

Consider the nature of the teenage relationship

1. All relationships may struggle after the birth of a child.
2. Can you identify the strengths in the teenage relationship?
3. What is the age of the father and what does he contribute in terms of social, financial and emotional support to his partner?
4. Are there opportunities to further encourage his involvement?

---

## 'A bit of poo and sick?'
## Young fathers in the domestic arena

### The domestic arena

Dominant discourses on young men do not often present them in a caring role; indeed constructions of young, white, working class masculinities often problematise young men as risk taking (Lloyd & Forrest 2001), for example, engaging in smoking, drinking, binge drinking, and sexual opportunism. In his account, based upon interviews with boys in comprehensive, grammar and independent schools, Barrowclough (1999) cites the attitude of Steve who became a father at 16. Steve attended a comprehensive school and left school with few qualifications:

> I was going out with lots of other girls when I was going out with Anna. I didn't really think of her as my girlfriend, although she thought I was her boyfriend. Of course I used to say I loved her, but I always said that to all the girls I went out with. You have to say you love a girl because then they let you have sex … when you're a fifteen year old boy all you want is sex with as many girls as possible. You don't want sex because you love someone, you have sex because you want sex.
>
> (Barrowclough 1999)

However, contrary to these popular risky images, some young men are involved in 'hidden' domestic support particularly when they become fathers (Reeves 2006) and although they often defer to the mother's overall key managerial role with the child(ren), they describe times and spaces which are their domain. For example night-time is described by many young men as a key time for their involvement.

**Case transcript**

**As Peter describes:**

Because what happens is, she will go to bed about 9 or 10pm, depending when he wants to go. Then I will stay up until about 3am, waiting for him to wake up for his 3am feed, give him his bottle, settle him down again while she is sleeping, I hope. And then I do that bit and she wakes up and does the next bit.

All of the young fathers in Reeves (2006) who described their involvement also revealed the apparent willingness with which their participation was given. They situated themselves as working in partnership with the mother of the child and distributing tasks between them. Perhaps most appealing is how they described being involved in caring for their child, a factor often not referred to in the literature and an image not usually associated with socially excluded young men. As Christie (2001) remarks from social work literature:

> Men as carers were both 'invisible' and 'ultra visible'; they became invisible when the gender assumptions by welfare workers excluded them as a potential source of informal care, yet those men who are identified as carers may be 'ultra visible' due to the gendered nature of most caring tasks. Discourses of welfare and social work, for the most part, represent men as either passive recipients of care or resistant recipients of control and not as active providers of care.
>
> (Christie 2001: 30)

**Case transcript**

**Mark describes how he has the main responsibility for his young disabled son:**

I wouldn't say I do everything, it's just, I don't know, I do him at night, all night, get up about five o'clock in the morning, or well she shoves me 'you going to get out of bed and sort him out' and I do housework and all. I don't do cooking, no I don't know how

> . . . I do the washing up and everything else. I bathe him, well basically I do everything but sometimes she does jump in and say like someone comes round say, like I don't know, my nan, she'll jump and do it just to show them and I can't do nothing about it. It's her word against my word at the end of the day. But I don't know I do love her, I do admit that.

For some young men fatherhood is not their first experience of caring, it can also have been a task carried out in their birth families. This portrayal of previous caring capacities in families could point to an underestimation of the amount young men do contribute in their birth and subsequent families. Of course generational patterns of fathering indicate that fathers in contemporary times are more likely to be involved with their children, though it is not a popular representation for young fathers (Tyrer *et al.* 2005). A point to note, however, is that the majority of the young fathers in the study by Reeves (2006) were unemployed, a feature which perhaps makes it easier to be involved at night and to catch up on rest during the day, a point taken up in Chapter 6 by Rosa Panades-Blas who develops the idea that teenage fatherhood contributes a further element to the debate on fatherhood generally.

## Case transcript

**Having a caring role is a position also described by Adam, who describes a past caring role with his sister.**

*Adam:* I don't mind a bit of poo and a bit of sick or whatever.

*Jane:* You've done it before?

*Adam:* Yeah with my little sister. My sister had whooping cough and I managed to deal with that. I was by myself by the side of her and she was at the toilet. I got used to that, I don't know I've just cleaned up the shit and poo and everything.

> **Good Practice Box**
>
> **Identify the skills the young father has with his children**
>
> 1. Has he had experience with children before?
> 2. What caring skills does he contribute to the family?
> 3. What was his role in his biological family?
> 4. Does he need to develop parenting or 'playing' skills or does he already have them?
> 5. Are there opportunities to further encourage his involvement?

## Prohibitive influences on young fathers; the role of the maternal grandparent

**The maternal grandparent**

Some evidence suggests that fathers generally who are engaged in a loving, sexual relationship with the mother of their children will interact more positively with their child (Furstenberg 1995, Lamb 1987, Lamb & Elster 1985, Parke 1996) and are more likely to be involved in family life on a long-term basis (see Chapter 6 on this debate). However, factors have been identified which significantly influence this involvement, including family approval or disapproval or emotional distancing (Weimann *et al.* 2006), cultural issues, whether the young man lives with his child or children and also the quality of his relationship with the baby's maternal grandmother.

- A study by Gavin *et al.* (2002) ascertained that young fathers are more likely to be involved with their child in families where the maternal grandmother had high education levels and where the father had a positive relationship with her.

- They found that the maternal grandmother often acts as a gatekeeper towards the father, either encouraging him towards adopting a positive role or keeping him at arm's length depending upon circumstances. Weinmann *et al.* (2006) have suggested that this is a particular trait found amongst white families. They explain:

Adolescent mothers frequently live with their own families during the first few years following birth . . . For families of some pregnant adolescents, prospective fathers are perceived as threatening to the newly found closeness that the pregnancy has spawned. Thus, some pregnant adolescents find themselves having to choose between parental support or support from their babies' fathers.

(Weinmann *et al.* 2006: 629–630)

Significantly the authors highlighted that father involvement at two weeks following the birth predicted ongoing, at least, monthly contact between a young father and his child in the future.

- Kalil *et al.* (2005) also point out in their longitudinal study that strong support from the maternal grandmother and, in particular, where she co-resided with the teenage mother was related to sustained low father involvement.

- It is also argued by Smith *et al.* (2001) that where the relationship with both the mother of his child and her mother has broken down, a young father needs help, not necessarily with looking after his child, but with communication and negotiation skills in the complex and sometimes hostile adult discussions regarding access to the child.

---

**Good Practice Box**

### Encouraging communication skills

Some young men may need encouragement to keep in contact with their child because of a lack of skills in negotiating with gatekeepers or significant people in their child's life, rather than always needing guidance in looking after their child.

---

## A positive force?
## The role of the paternal grandmother

**The paternal grandmother**

My nan's like my carer because my mum's not here. If anything's got to go wrong I just got to go there. I go there quite often and talk to her and that.' Mark, aged 18.

There is a particular dearth of studies which consider the influence and support of a young father's birth family on the pregnancy and birth of his baby. Indeed, in comparison to the literature on the changing relationship between a young woman and her mother following the birth of a child (Allen & Dowling 1998, Oakely 1979, Reeves 2003, Tabberer *et al.* 2000) the relationship between a young father and his mother is currently under-researched. Fagan *et al.* (2007) emphasise the crucial link of family members in encouraging the relationship between a young father and his child. Adopting a stress model they outline that young fathers are often exposed to multiple stress factors, including their own health, social isolation, depression, role restriction, partnership difficulties and parent/child attachment issues. These stress factors can be additive and combined with the emotion of parenthood the situation can become overwhelming for a young man. Support from his birth family can be crucial in reducing the risk to the father/child relationship. Chapter 6 considers that there are particular factors of stress associated with young fatherhood which need to be acknowledged.

In Reeves' (2006) study, three young men, Ben, Paul and Andy, describe how important their mothers are to them and portray how they have offered them ongoing practical and emotional support following the birth of their child. Ben positions his mother as central to his daily life and describes the attachment he has with her and describes her as helping out with his current baby and also in preparing Ben and his partner for the birth of their second child. Similarly Paul portrays that he and his mother have always been close and this mutually supportive relationship has

## Case transcript

**Andy describes using his mother as part of his network of support as a young father.**

The screaming of Sofia and her temper tantrums, even now it gets to me and it really makes me want to strangle her, you know it makes me want to shake her. So I can understand how people have done it. I got to the point where I thought no, this ain't right, this is wrong and I cried because I felt that way and I phoned my mum and she said 'yes I felt that with you'. So I phoned a few people, so I got to learn to phone a few people to calm down, have a break, walk outside, have a drink.

continued following the birth of his child. As practitioners working in services with a maternal focus (Daniel & Taylor 1999, 2001) it can be easy to focus on the isolated teenage unit, forgetting previous longer-term relationships in young people's lives. It is crucial that these relationships are acknowledged and assessed.

---

**Good Practice Box**

**Assess the contribution that maternal and paternal grandparents bring to the lives of young fathers**

1. Who are the main providers of support to the family?
2. Where does the young father get his support from?
3. Is he close to his mother or are there other siblings who provide support?

---

## Other influences on young fathers: a care history

**Other influences**

Although some young men do have positive family relationships which can be drawn on, some may have a criminal or care history which may prohibit them drawing on their family support networks. In the study by Tyrer *et al.* (2005) their findings set out the social exclusion and disadvantage that most of the young fathers described experiencing especially with 'little financial security, low educational achievement and poor work prospects' (2005: 1110). In addition, the young men emphasised their poor experiences of the care system and how their perceived complex support needs were not addressed by staff, in an industry with a particularly high staff turnover.

A large body of research suggests that being in and leaving the care system exposes young people to fast-track transitions, especially when compared to young people who grow up and leave the family home at their own pace (Allen 2003, Biehal & Wade 1996, Corlyon & McGuire 1997). Inman (2001) remarks that this accelerated move towards adulthood is often compounded by young people's experiences in care and, as a consequence, adds to their vulnerability when leaving.

Allen (2003) takes up this point in her small-scale study of young people leaving the care system. She remarks that the reasons a young person enters the care system can often influence the quality of their post-16 transition experience. She states that for the young people in her study, 'Care history affected young people's ability to build and maintain significant relationships, their schooling, and their attitudes and self esteem' (Allen 2003: viii). Many of the young people in Allen's study left school and the care system with few qualifications and poor job prospects, which increased their exposure to financial problems and worries. Support was cited as a key ingredient of post-16 success, and those young people with family or long-term professional relationships formed whilst in care, were more likely to adapt and cope with the challenges of independence. Allen argues that transitoriness in relationships, employment and support increased the likelihood of the journey to adulthood breaking down.

Similarly, Biehal and Wade (1996) concluded from their study that care leavers' experiences of the transition to adulthood are 'both accelerated and compressed' (1996:45). Their two-stage study included the views of both young women and young men, with the authors remarking on the vulnerability of the young people in their study, particularly to becoming parents and forming their own families. These findings have been borne out by more recent studies (Allen 2003, Corlyon & McGuire 1997) which further emphasise the importance of support for young people leaving care, specifically support that is responsive, ongoing, flexible and 'tailored to their needs' (Allen 2003: ix). Very often it is highlighted that young people leaving care try to re-establish relationships with family members (Biehal & Wade 1996) and this can be fraught with difficulties, often similar to those that occurred when the young person came into care initially.

The implication for young men who become fathers who have been in the care system, therefore, is that they often do not have family support mechanisms to draw on when they become parents (or these relationships are damaged). This can be important for day to day support when the young man is resident with his child(ren). However, with the fragility of teenage relationships, the consequence of not having close family support can be that if the relationship ends, potential mediators with the mother and maternal grandparents can be thin on the ground. As Tyrer *et al.* (2005) suggest, despite there being some positive emotions

**Routing**

**Sorting**
**Y07A06X**
**Covering — BXXXX**
**Despatch**

268323970 UKRWLG40 RC1

| Ship To: | UK 00849001 F |
| --- | --- |

LAMBETH PCT
LAMBETH AND SOUTHWARK HEA
FIRST FLOOR
1 LOWER MARSH
WATERLOO
SE1 7NT

**Volume:**
**Edition:**
**Year:** 2008
**Coutts CN:** 8802262

| ISBN | Qty | Sales Order |
| --- | --- | --- |
| 9781905539291 | 1 | F 9844388   1 |

| Customer P/O No | Cust P/O List |
| --- | --- |
| 12 SEP 08 | 27.00 GBP |

Title: Inter–professional Approach to Young
Fathers / edited

**Format:** P (Paperback)
**Author:** Reeves, Jane
**Publisher:** M&K Update Ltd
**Fund:**
**Location:**
**Loan Type:**

Order Specific Instructions

**COUTTS INFORMATION SERVICES LTD.:**

associated with becoming a young father who has experienced the care system, they conclude:

> While experiences of social exclusion, bureaucracy and hassle and distant fathering may be common to young fathers from disadvantaged backgrounds, evidence from this study suggests that time spent in public care may compress these factors by making it hard for men to build trusting relationships important for successful fathering.
>
> (Tyrer *et al.* 2005: 1119)

## Complex family relationships

**Complex relationships**

Forming a new partnership and having a baby often encourage the formation of new relationships in wider family and social networks (Laub & Sampson 2003). This process is similar for teenage parents, although often these new relationships are constructed under difficult circumstances. For example Jay draws attention to the complex relationships, dynamics and emotions that can occur when a partnership turns into 'parentship' for a young couple:

### Case transcript

*Jay:* Well it's hard, its very weird grounds like, they don't know me from Adam to Eve. I'm with their daughter and we've got a baby. Last they knew their girlfriend, their daughter I mean was seventeen years old and living in a hostel, now she's eighteen , got a new born baby. So it's very hard to get to know them, her dad, John, he's a lovely man, very blunt which I like in a person. But my point is, if for instance I do something she disagrees with, like I held my baby once in her house like because I used to visit their house and I was winding him and everything. It was a bit weird, she went to me 'oh you don't do it like this' and she took him off me and just turned him around and put him on his belly. Now it's nothing to me but at the time she had no place to tell me that, but her mum is a nice lady and she's helped us out. I can't diss the fact that she gave us those frames there, them picture frames, them two and her dad took all them photos except that one, paid thirty quid for that one. I got that one free down Alders. Yeah they are nice people, they've given us cups and helped us out..

The case of Jay, above, identifies several dilemmas. His description portrays his indecisiveness about his partner's parents primarily focused on the imbalance of power between them. On the one hand he appears greatly relieved that they seem to have accepted him and are offering his new family emotional and practical support, although he mentions they are hard to get to know. On the other hand, he admits that he does not like being told what to do, especially regarding the care of his own child. However, Jay acknowledges he is not the person who holds power in this situation. Due to his stated inability to cope with his child he is in the uncomfortable 'forced' position (Harre & Langenhove 1999), initiated by social services, of having to comply with their arrangements and this includes the involvement of his partner's parents in the care and protection of the baby. Legislation and policy are key factors for practitioners and students considering the position of young fathers. Key elements of legislation and policy are considered in detail in Chapters 2 and 5.

Other young fathers also describe undergoing this process, with varying degrees of strain and anxiety. Specifically, Manuel, Dwayne and Victor describe how they set about forming positive relationships with their partner's parents and trying to make investments for the future in new social networks.

- Manuel describes how he and his partner see her parents 'every day', how he has invested his feelings in the relation-ships with them and how the relationship is mutually supportive. He places his partner's parents in a position of high regard, expressing his love for them: 'I love them to pieces, they are like my own parents, they are great, they really are.'

- Dwayne describes living with his partner's grandmother who is portrayed as taking him in when his step-father 'threw him out'. He relates his affection for her and describes how she looks after him: 'Buys me like tracksuit bottoms, baggy shirt and like a jumper every week, or like every other week, something like that.'

**Case transcript**

## Victor

For Victor, aged 16, lacking in parental support of his own, locating himself within his partner's family appears tricky, but necessary. He tells how his partner's parents found out about the pregnancy:

*Victor:* He came in to the room and said 'are you going to tell me the good news?' and she didn't say anything, but we thought he might have known because he, Sharron went 'I'm getting fat ain't I ?' and he went 'yeah in one place'. He walked in to the bathroom and she was being sick and said 'everything's going to be OK' so that's why we thought he knew, but I might be wrong, don't know yet. He doesn't seem like he's all mad and that . . . I get on with her dad, I really like him and every time I go down there, he's always got something new to teach me . . . like yesterday he was talking about how fast the world travels, how far away the sun is, it's something like seventy-three million miles away.

The maternal grandparent, then, often acts as a gatekeeper between the young father, the mother and the baby (Gavin *et al.* 2002). Some young fathers, however, tell of other gatekeeping relationships, particularly where the young mother has a fairly positive relationship with her parents. Victor, in the episode above, appears to be taking the line of least resistance. Thus, rather than acting the pregnancy scenario out as a conflict, Victor curries favour with his partner's father, acknowledging his role as a teacher.

There would therefore seem to be a process of re-negotiation for all parties following a pregnancy at a young age, not just between a young mother and her own mother (Tabberer *et al.* 2000) or the young father and her mother (Gavin *et al.* 2002) but also between the young father and his partner's father. The process can often be highly emotional but one which needs to be navigated carefully by all parties involved. Acknowledging this as a potential hurdle to young fathers and encouraging them or increasing their communication skills could be a positive step in working with young fathers.

> **Good Practice Box**
>
> Identify the relationships a young father has with his wider family
>
> 1. What are the strengths of the relationships?
> 2. Can you identify any tensions or weaknesses in these relationships? Do they need to be re-negotiated?
> 3. Can anything be done to foster more positive relationships?

As Figure 1.1 sets out, a young father, particularly if he has biological children from previous relationships, can have a complex myriad of social interactions many of which have potential barriers associated with them, for example barriers of hostility, communication and geography. If a young man has a care history he may have a poor relationship with his own biological parents and/or siblings. Moreover, if he has children with whom he does not live, then he may be faced with obstacles to overcome in seeing them, perhaps through the relationship he has with his previous partner(s) or her mother. In addition, very often a young man does not have access to services in his own right, as statutory health and social care services are often maternally focused. Viewed in this way a young father can have limited support options on offer. Consequently, professional support can become of increased significance.

## Challenging negative discourses: the importance of professional support

**Negative discourses**

As this chapter has sought to emphasise, the lives of young fathers are often complex; there are often a myriad of social relationships and responsibilities which need to be faced, as well as accepting the challenge of becoming a new father. Levels of complexity will therefore increase with subsequent relationships and successive children.

Cavanagh and Cree (1996) argue that discourses within social welfare are not gender neutral. They suggest that particular practices and responses are legitimised and normalised, often reinforcing traditionally perceived, stereotypical boundaries

**Figure 1.1**     **Inter-relationship of networks for young fathers**

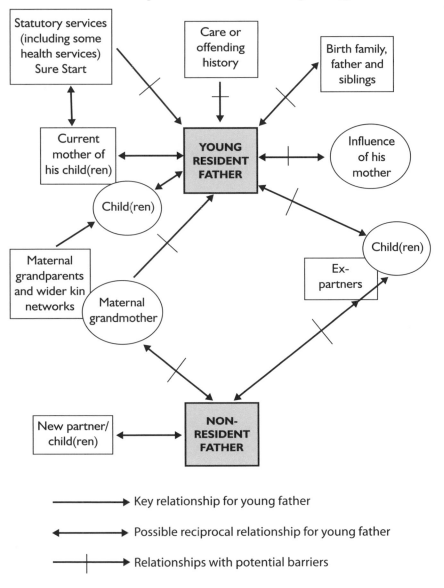

between men and women, with men seen as providers and women as carers. Bowl (2001) argues that central to the welfare framework in the UK is the Beveridge derived discourse, in which men are seen as primarily the providers of material goods and not as the providers of care.

From a feminist perspective, Christie (2001) and Daniel and Taylor (2001) remark that patriarchal practices within contemporary welfare service provision are normalised by social work practice, even within anti-discriminatory and anti-oppressive working practice, in relation to reinforcing boundaries between men and women. This is also a theme which resonates in the practices of midwives, health visitors and other health care practitioners. Men are often presented as having little involvement in the emotional life of the family. Feminist views on the position and role of men as service users in social work would argue that caring is still essentially feminised and this has implications for the way men interact with their families when they are receiving services, or when they need to ask for help, and how practitioners respond to and work with men (O'Brian 2004).

O'Brian (2004) and Daniel and Taylor (2001) argue that the majority of fathers tend to be absent from interactions between practitioners and families, as much 'social work' or health visiting takes place during the day when men may be at work or absent from the family home. Professional environments may also not be seen as conducive to the involvement of men.

## Sure Start and Young Fathers

**Sure Start**

One key organisation which focuses upon the needs of young parents and tries to actively engage with young fathers is Sure Start. Sure Start is a major government initiative: a flagship service to give young children living in communities of high need a better start in life and their parents greater resources of hope. Sure Start is central to the government's childcare strategy. The Chancellor of the Exchequer introduced the Sure Start programme in July 1998 as part of the government's strategy to end child poverty by 2020:

> We plan to bring together quality services for the under 3s and their parents – nursery, childcare and play group provision, and pre-natal and other services. One new feature will be to extend to parents the offer of counselling and help to prepare their children for learning and for school.
>
> (HM Treasury, July 1998: 5)

Local Sure Start Programmes (LSSPs) were developed in 1999 (Glass 1999) to improve the health and well-being of children age 0–4 years and their families so that they would have a greater opportunity to flourish when they started school. Sure Start is a cross-departmental programme. Its aim is 'to work with parents-to-be, parents and children to promote the physical, intellectual and social development of babies and young children – particularly those who are disadvantaged – to ensure that they can flourish at home and when they get to school, and thereby break the cycle of disadvantage for the current generation of young children'. In the 2002 spending review 500 local Sure Start programs were guaranteed until 2013 (Ward 2002). Sure Start is part of the Labour government's drive to modernise public services, to focus on targets and achievement of outcomes and an expectation that professional and other staff members will work together more collaboratively, or in a more 'joined up' way, to ensure better outcomes for children and more effective use of resources.

The service aimed to provide better access to family support, advice on nurturing, health services and early learning, through a partnership involving local authorities, health practitioners, parents and voluntary and community organisations (Sure Start Unit 2002: 94). LSSPs targeted local disadvantaged communities rather than 'at risk children' and families. The initiative reflected the government's concern with pockets of deprivation where the problems of unemployment and crime were said to be acute and hopelessly tangled up with poor health, housing and education (Social Exclusion Unit 1998).

Local partnerships were integral to how LSSPs would be delivered. In the majority of programmes management board committees were formed. The membership of these partnership programmes generally included local authorities, including representation of county and district councils, police authorities, NHS Trusts, local parents, business people, charities and community groups. All partner members were given equal say in policy development.

The aims of the Sure Start unit in England are outlined on the following page.

---

**Sure Start Local Programme in England**

Aim and Public Services Agreement (PSA)
Targets for 2001/02 – 2003/03

Aim: To work with parents-to-be, parents and children, to promote the physical, intellectual and social development of babies and children – particularly those who are disadvantaged – so that they can flourish at home and when they get to school, and thereby breaking the cycle of disadvantage for the current generation of young children.

**Target – Improving Social and Emotional Development**
Reduce the proportion of children aged 0–3 years who are re-registered within the space of 12 months on the child protection register by 20 per cent by 2004.

**Target – Improving Health**
Achieve by 2004 a 10 per cent reduction in mothers who smoke in pregnancy.

**Target – Improving the Ability to Learn**
Achieve by 2004, for children aged 0–3 years, a reduction of five percentage points in the number of children with speech and language problems requiring specialist intervention by the age of four.

**Target – Strengthening Families**
Reduce the number of 0–3-year-olds living in households where no one is working.

---

(Sure Start Unit 2002)

## The collection of data

There is a requirement by all centres to undertake evaluation and monitoring. Specific data was collected by Sure Start Units, including the numbers of children and parents seen, numbers of ante-natal referrals, numbers of employed parents, numbers of children with disabilities and the ethnic background of parents. There was also an emphasis on the percentage of children seen in different age groups either through outreach or attendance at centres. From the collection of this data the numbers of children and families within LSSPs were therefore known; consequently, there was also evidence of the percentage of children and parents not seen. It was through experience that it became apparent that fathers were not as likely to attend LSSP Centres as mothers. However, a study examining the involvement of fathers found that they had a preference for fun and active sessions over discussion based ones, and staff indicated that it was easier to involve fathers in outdoor, active fun-day type activities than indoor sessions with children or in sessions related to parenting skills (Lloyd *et al.* 2003).

## Sure Start at Millmead – overcoming initial problems

Sure Start Millmead was developed in 2000/01. Millmead is a public housing estate situated on the outskirts of Margate in the District of Thanet on the North Eastern corner of Kent. Thanet is the second most deprived district in the South East region. On any conventional measure of economic development, poverty and low morale, Thanet struggles, the estate of Millmead especially. In the literature it has been described as a classic 'sink estate' with high proportions of single parent families and long-term unemployed and in one view has the 'worst reputation' of any part of Thanet (Buck *et al.* 1990).

Unemployment for many is long-term while those who enter employment find themselves in low paid, low skilled jobs. Educationally, Millmead struggles with 65% of the local residents having a reading age of seven or less. There was a long history of consultation regarding services and unfulfilled promises on the estate at the start of the Sure Start programme. Residents were sceptical and cynical. There was little confidence in state service provision.

## Planning a strategy

When planning our parent participation strategy we were mindful of the following:

- the nature of Thanet in general and Millmead in particular
- the history of unfulfilled promises in relation to the building of a local community centre and secondary school

- the high levels of poverty
- the fear of crime and the high levels of domestic violence
- the degree of social isolation
- the lack of confidence in statutory service provision
- the low level of aspiration in the community
- the low literacy levels
- the low levels of confidence and self esteem in parents generally.

The strategy was planned as a team which included parents from the area, aiming to provide a range of different experiences for parents and children, over a one-year period initially. Events were planned in a systematic way covering each month of the year. Days and times varied to accommodate what we perceived as local needs. Our strategy was underpinned by two concepts:

**Food** was provided at all participation events. At the early stages of the programme parents often prepared the food or did barbeques. They also shopped for the food and prepared buffet style meals. Food was often prepared by a group of parents and then shared with the larger group. All left over food was given to parents and children to take home. Different types of food were prepared and children and families had the opportunity to try out those foods which they may not have been able to afford or purchase locally.

All participation events and services generally within the programme were free. These included trips to the local Farming World, Rare Breed Sanctuary, zoo, Margate beach and Canterbury.

Bouncy castles, circus activities, story telling, musical instruments, messy play were regular features in our fun days. Parents too were encouraged to have fun in playing with their children and being involved in activities.

**Examples of what was planned include:**

- Easter Egg Hunt in local park for all the family
- Teddy Bear's Picnic in the park for the whole family
- summer outing to Farming World for the whole family
- Breastfeeding Awareness Trip to Margate in partnership with other local Sure Start Programme
- fishing trip aimed at fathers
- bowling trip aimed at fathers

- football team development in partnership with Charlton Athletic Football Club
- science trip to the park where children were helped to use magnifying glasses to examine insects and flora
- summer barbeque in the park
- women's netball team development
- trip to local allotment project with all family members
- Halloween parties – so popular we needed to have three
- Christmas parties in partnership with Pfizer who provided a quality Christmas present to all named children
- disco aimed at young children and their parents
- Messy Play Day – where parents and children could play with a range of messy materials and liquids.

Each event was evaluated and a report was written and shared. Details of all children and parents who attended were recorded. All suggestions from parents and staff on how to improve for future events were taken on board and used for future planning and this was done through the completion of evaluation forms. We knew from information on attendance who was attending and who we were failing to engage. The level of participation was discussed on a weekly basis in our large integrated team meeting. The need for outreach support from Community Workers to engage with the hardest to reach families and groups was evident. Strategies were developed to ensure all families not accessing our services received regular home visits.

Community workers are key to engaging parents, including the young and vulnerable. Many of these workers are parents who have been locally recruited and trained. They have local knowledge and are respected and trusted by the local community. They want to see things change and improve in their community and are prepared to work hard to ensure local services meet the needs of the community. Community workers offer home visits in the antenatal period and also after the baby is born.

## The role of community workers

Sure Start Millmead emphasises the importance of outreach home visiting. The role of community workers was developed and piloted in the programme.

**The key responsibilities of community workers are:**

- to offer support, friendship and commitment to identified families in the area
- to seek out parents' views, including fathers, on needs and service developments
- initially to advocate on behalf of parents, including fathers, ensuring the views of parents are heard within the Team
- to encourage and empower parents, including fathers, to recognise their own skills
- to provide a befriending service through outreach home visits to families at agreed times, working in partnership with professionals
- to support residents of Millmead and St Peter's in their parenting role in line with objectives, i.e. attachment, play, communication, safety
- to contribute to identifying the needs of the local parents, including fathers, and children and help with the organisation and development of parent networks and groups to meet these needs
- to work in partnership with other agencies and professionals, e.g. Health Visitors, Midwives, Community Social Workers.

## Issues specific to the engagement of fathers in Sure Start

There are several points which need to be considered when engaging with men. These are listed below.

- Some fathers stated they lacked confidence to speak in a group of fathers.
- They preferred being in a mixed group (with their partner/wife) as then the emphasis was not on them to keep the conversation flowing.
- Some felt self-conscious in the programme as most parents who attended groups were mothers.
- Some did not want to be treated differently because they were fathers.
- Most fathers preferred to see a female community worker as they felt they were more skilled than a male volunteer who was

available to support them.

- Many Sure Start fathers do not like football and did not wish to be stereotyped.

- Some fathers felt uncomfortable about domestic violence services being promoted in the centre as for them this meant 'male violence on women.'

- Some fathers stated they did not want to be singled out and praised or acknowledged for attending; in this respect they wanted to be treated the same as the mothers.

- Most fathers were not comfortable talking about their feelings.

- All fathers wanted to be involved in their child's learning and care.

- Fathers were most comfortable in the programme when doing hands on activities with their children such as arts and crafts, face painting and messy play.

- Fathers enjoyed spending a day with their child in the nursery.

- Fathers enjoyed outdoor play activities with their children.

- Some fathers were elected as Community Representatives on the Management Board and attended meetings on a regular basis.

- Fathers stated they liked the ethos of the Sure Start programme as it was child focused.

- Some fathers wanted Sure Start services to be available over the weekend.

- The Sure Start Dads Group has run for many years originally set up as a 'Dad and Toddler' group providing ongoing support and a place for fathers to meet.

- Young fathers informed us that they wanted to be involved in their child's care.

- Some young fathers felt 'left out' by their partners after the birth of the baby.

- Some young fathers felt that it was OK to attend Sure Start groups as long as their 'mates' did not know.

- Some young fathers said they did not feel welcome in antenatal clinics and antenatal classes during their partner's pregnancy.

- Many young fathers had poor literacy and numeracy skills and are dependent on their partners or their parents to support them with this.

- Most young fathers had few qualifications and were employed in low skilled casual work.
- Young fathers attended the Internet café and supported others with IT issues.
- Young fathers attended baby massage sessions.
- Many young fathers are members of MCCPL a Social Enterprise.
- Young fathers play in the local football team.

### Men Talk:
### Extracts from Sure Start Millmead's Local Evaluation

Andy attended Sure Start Children's Centre services. Andy described himself as a sensitive man. He had always wanted to be a father. He worried about his wife's frequent bouts of depression. She struggled, he said with taking to child rearing and became angry, demanding his attention by, for example, phoning whilst he was at work and demanding he returned home. He tried to be supportive and told himself that 'there will always be another job, not another family'. Families were fragile affairs which made him want to be a good dad.

'You know it was a macho thingy there, but I had become very protective of her and I wanted to be there to make sure she was always alright. So I would be there when she was throwing up in the morning with morning sickness – I wanted to be there. You know I didn't want to be . . . I didn't want to feel like I was going to be a part-time dad. I wanted to be there 24x7; I wanted to be there.'

John admitted to feeling uncomfortable with some of the parents on the estate. He did not want his own children 'integrating' with particular families, and wanted Sure Start as a project involving 'like minded' parents that care about their children. He also liked Sure Start because 'it was completely female in surroundings, but I suppose I wasn't weeded out as much for what some fellas might have been because of my previous life: I was brought up with women and I was integrated into that . . . my parents would have had their friends around and I would be sitting in the kitchen with them. So it has never bothered me. I have made friends out of females a hell of a lot more than men. I feel more comfortable in that surrounding, so it didn't bother me a bit.'

Chris talked about Sure Start as a feminine space and felt embarrassment and terror at the thought of going to women's territory . . . women and their activities. 'There's the Parent and Toddler, but men didn't do that, it's namby pamby. Not being funny, but you know . . .' Moreover, he would not, he said, take his children to the Parent and Toddler group.

'If there were more men then yes, I would go, because it is female dominated as far as I understand it. I consider, because I knew they will be watching me, watching the way I am with the kids. I feel they will be judgmental. I knew it would happen, guarantee it. It is like if there was a men's group, I would be watching you like a hawk, seriously I would. Thinking 'are you the same as us, or you just trying to barge in?' See what I am saying, that is why I am thinking about the women and the way they are going to be thinking 'oh isn't he a good father' and all this sort of stuff, even though I know I am a good father and I think I have done pretty well for those years, bringing up these two.

Chris became involved with Sure Start following an incident on the estate in which there had been a fatality. Chris had been personally involved with a particular family.

'It was someone from Sure Start, the social worker. She helped me and one of the ladies. She came down to see the girls. Not social services, they just came around to say hello and how are you . . . because it was a pretty bad time for me then . . . we saw what was going on . . . for the first couple of months afterwards I couldn't sleep at all. I was on tablets. I couldn't really take them because the kids couldn't sleep as well. All I kept thinking was this going to happen to us? And so I obviously couldn't allow myself to take the tablets just in case they did get me to sleep and they kept me asleep.'

Sure Start had been 'brilliant' in providing desperately needed support, especially the community workers.

Chris was born near London and his mother and father divorced at a 'very young age'. He moved to the Sure Start area as a child and later 'I moved back with my partner and two kids. It wasn't much of a life. I went to the local school, it was called the workshops. The curriculum there was very poor, terrible, all they were really interested in was exams and there was no support at all and if you didn't want to learn then they wouldn't pressurise you into learning. For instance they asked me if I wanted to take my English exam and I said no and I didn't ever take it, which to me is wrong'.

(West & Wenham 2003)

The Family Policy Studies Centre in 1996 indicated that, despite all the rhetoric, childcare remained overwhelmingly a maternal affair. Men and women alike continue to regard 'mother' as the central player in children's lives (Forma 1999). In communities like Millmead where fathers often have not got the skill base to access employment, mothers who are often single parents find themselves taking on the role of the breadwinner, by taking on low paid part-time work. Fathers have been identified as 'hard to reach' in the context of Sure Start programmes.

There is evidence that some fathers are unsure of their role in children's centres and some are anxious about accessing services as they fear they will be judged negatively on their parenting skills. Fathers would feel more confident about accessing services in children's centres if there were more fathers present. Many fathers enjoy being part of a children's centre and are comfortable in a child focused feminine space.

## Problems engaging with young fathers

Practitioners in the study by Higginbottom *et al.* (2006) on Black Minority Ethnic young parents explained that young fathers are often marginalised, both in hospital based midwifery services and when seeking advice, commenting that the services were always geared up to 'mums' rather than to both partners.

O'Brian (2004) suggests that an inability to engage with men or to isolate them creates distance, often positioning men away from problems within the family and detracting from men's participation in creating effective solutions. Moreover, he argues that dominant discourses of masculinity affect men's identities and the way they behave. For example, contemporary 'hegemonic' constructions of masculinity suggest that men often repress feelings and emotions, weaknesses and symptoms (Connell 1995, 2000).

In a study by Williams (1999), although men cited strong feelings of love towards their children, they explained they did not always find these feelings easy to express. O'Brian (2004) argues that this emotional reluctance can lead to men only becoming involved with social services when requested by their partner or when the issue is deemed very serious, for example, when care proceedings are going to be initiated.

Chapter 4 considers some of the implications of working and engaging with young fathers in the early days of the pregnancy, through the birth and beyond, and how crucial work at this early stage can harness young men into positive professional relationships in the future.

## Dominant professional discourses

There are a number of dominant discourses relating to men as service users which may affect how social workers and other professionals conceptualise and 'position' men, albeit unconsciously in their interactions with them (Daniel & Taylor 2001; Featherstone 2003). These conceptions can fundamentally impact upon how professionals connect with young fathers.

### Seeing men as 'risks'

Daniel and Taylor (2001) argue that the threat and reality of domestic violence and child abuse is a powerful presence in social work practice, casting a 'monolithic' shadow over interactions between social workers and men, and often affecting how they are worked with. Research reviewed by Daniel and Taylor (2001) and Hester *et al.* (2000) reinforces the idea that for children witnessing and enduring violence towards self, siblings or mother, is extremely negative and can influence future behaviour and self esteem. Violence and the threat of violence by men towards women and children is a theme firmly embedded within social work, health visiting and the legal system in the UK (Adams *et al.* 1998).

Daniel and Taylor (2001) outline that the statutory social services still tend to look to the mother and her ability to protect her children in relation to child protection and intervention strategies. Featherstone (2003) and Daniel and Taylor (2001) argue that the threat and practice of violence, as well as sexual abuse by men towards women and children, leads to social workers not 'engaging directly with the fathers who are causing the problem in the first place' (Daniel & Taylor 2001: 161). Moreover, Stanley (1997) argues that the consequence of this practice is that men become 'invisible', with the result that they are not worked with and are not considered part of the equation. Coulshed and Orme (1998) suggest that as the majority of social workers (health visitors and midwives) on the ground are female, this considera-tion also influences practice.

Adams *et al.* (1998) argue that risk is real for all practitioners working with vulnerable families, but the perpetuation of the idea that all men are potential risks and the continuation of this as a dominant professional discourse in health and social care, may contribute to men not being assessed appropriately or at all (O'Hagan & Dillenberger 1995). Positioning men, albeit unconsciously, in a negative way or not considering them at all, allows men little room for manoeuvre or response. On the other hand encouraging involvement, by adopting a 'father sensitive evaluation' (O'Brian 2004) may introduce less negative discourses which may be of greater help in practice. The pervasiveness of this discourse in turn seems to affect the child care practices of young fathers.

## Seeing men as 'no use'

Another dominant discourse within health and social care which potentially prohibits the positive involvement of many fathers is the idea of men as 'no use'. Daniel and Taylor (1999, 2001) argue that this discourse is perceived to have its roots in the maternal welfarist perspective cited previously, that women are 'naturally' carers and men providers and the influence of this discourse is further entrenched due to the continuing influence of attachment theory (Daniel & Taylor 1999, 2001). The main strands of this argument include the continued tendency by practitioners to see the mother in the role of protector to her children and the main focus for intervention. In addition, the increasing fragmentation of families, with reconstituted partnerships and new relationships, can lead to confusion over status regarding biological and co-habiting fathers (O'Brian 2004) again reinforcing the central role of the mother in a changing landscape of relationships.

> **Good Practice Box**
>
> **Thinking about professional discourses and young fathers**
>
> Are there any procedures and practices in place which potentially exclude young fathers?
>
> What initiatives exist for young fathers?
>
> Are there any key practitioners/groups who work exclusively with this group of young men?
>
> How can practitioners adopt a more inclusive approach with this group?

## Conclusions and implications for professional practice

This chapter has considered some of the underlying issues relating to young fathers and provides an introduction to some of the wider debates continued in the following chapters. Significantly, the chapter has argued that young fathers and their support networks often need to be identified and assessed in their own right, in addition to those of the teenage mother. Many young fathers are involved in the physical and emotional care of their children and sometimes they need to draw on the support mechanisms and longstanding relationships outside of their partnership. However, it is important for professionals to recognise that the lives of some young men are complex and that serial relationships may well have resulted in them fathering more than one child. Consequently, their personal relationships can be multifaceted and they may need help, not necessarily with parenting their child but also negotiating access to their children through many 'gatekeeping' relationships which may exist and may form barriers to them interacting with their child(ren).

### Young fathers and support: key messages from research

The following key points should be kept in mind when working to support young fathers:

- fewer incidents of reported domestic violence than with 'older' fathers (Harner 2004)
- increase in importance of the male partner over time (Bunting & McAuley 2004)
- willingness to support the mother financially and emotionally in comparison to older fathers (Reeves 2003)
- participation in 'hidden' domestic chores related to their children (Reeves 2006)
- a positive relationship with the maternal grandmother and grandfather can aid his relationship with his child (Reeves 2006; Gavin *et al.* 2002)
- the importance of his own familial and social networks (Reeves 2006)
- the importance of a young father's relationship with his own mother (Reeves 2006)
- wider societal discourses in social welfare are not gender neutral (Cavanagh & Cree 1996)
- the negative discourses in specific agencies which marginalise men – men seen as 'risks' and 'no use' etc. (Featherstone 2003)
- professional practices which may covertly exclude young men (Reeves 2006).

# References

Adams, R., Dominelle, L. & Payne, M. (eds.) (1998). *Social Work: Themes, Issues and Critical Debates*. Basingstoke: Macmillan Press.

Allen, I. & Dowling, S. (1998). *Teenage Mothers: Decisions and Outcomes*. London: Policy Studies Institute.

Allen, M. (2003). *Into the Mainstream – Care Leavers Entering Work, Education and Training*. York: Joseph Rowntree Foundation.

Barrowclough, A. (1999). 'Boys Talk' in *The Times* 26 July: 37–38

Biehal, N. & Wade, J. (1996). 'Looking back, looking forward: Care leavers, families and change' in *Children and Youth Services Review* 18(4/5): 425–445.

Bowl, R. (2001). 'Men and community care' in Christie, A. (ed.) *Men and Social Work: Theories and Practices*. Basingstoke: Palgrave, pp. 109–125.

Buck, N., Gordon, I., Pucknance, C. & Taylor-Gooby, P. (1990). 'Isle of Thanet: restructuring and Municipal Conservatism' in Cooke, P. (ed.) *Localities*. London: Unwin and Hyman, pp.166–197.

Bunting, L. & McAuley, C. (2004). 'Teenage pregnancy and motherhood: The contribution of support' in *Child and Family Social Work* 9 (2): 207–215.

Cavanagh, K. & Cree, V. (eds.) (1996). *Working with Men: Feminism and Social Work*. London: Routledge.

Christie, A. (2001). *Men and Social Work: Theories and Practices*. Basingstoke: Palgrave.

Connell, R. (1995). *Masculinities*. Cambridge: Polity Press.

Connell, R.W. (2000). *The Men and the Boys*. Oxford: Polity Press.

Corlyon, J. & McGuire, C. (1997). Young Parents in Public Care. London: National Children's Bureau.

Coulshed, V. & Orme, J. (1998). *Social Work Practice: An Introduction*. Basingstoke: Palgrave.

Daniel, B. & Taylor, J. (1999). 'The rhetoric vs. the reality: A critical perspective on practice with fathers in child care and protection work' in *Child and Family Social Work* 4(3) August: 209–221.

Daniel, B. & Taylor, J. (2001). *Engaging with Fathers: Practice Issues for Health and Social Care*. London: Jessica Kingsley.

Fagan, J., Bernd, E. & Whiteman, V. (2007). 'Adolescent fathers' parenting stress, social support, and involvement with infants' in *Journal of Research on Adolescence* 17(1): 1–22.

Featherstone, B. (2003). 'Taking fathers seriously' in *British Journal of Social Work* 33: 239–254.

Firminger, K.B. (2006). 'Is he boyfriend material? Representation of males in teenage girls' magazines' in *Men and Masculinities* 8(3): 298–308.

Forma, A. (1999). *Mother of All Myths: How Society Moulds and Constrains Mothers*. London: Harper-Collins

Furstenberg, F. (1995). 'Fathering in the Inner City' in Marsiglio, W. (ed.) *Fatherhood, Contemporary Theory, Research and Social Policy*. Thousand Oakes: Sage Publications, pp. 119–147.

Gavin, L.E., Black, M.M., Minor, S., Abel, Y., Papas, M. & Bentley, M. (2002). 'Young, disadvantaged fathers' involvement with their infants: An ecological perspective' in *Journal of Adolescent Health* 31(3) September: 266–276.

Glass, N. (1999). 'Sure Start: the development of an early intervention programme for young children in the United Kingdom' in *Children & Society* 13(4): 257–264.

Harner, H.M. (2004). 'Domestic violence and trauma care in teenage pregnancy: Does paternal age make a difference?' in *Journal of Obstetric, Gynecologic and Neonatal Nursing* 33(3) May-June: 312–319.

Harre, R. & Langenhove, L.V. (1999). *Positioning Theory: Moral Contexts of Intentional Action*. Oxford: Blackwell Publishers.

Hester, M., Pearson, C. & Harwin, N. (2000). *Making an Impact: Children and Domestic Violence*. London: Jessica Kingsley Publishers.

Higginbottom, G.M.A., Mathers, N., Marsh, P., Kirkham, M., Owen, J.M. & Serrant-Green, L. (2006). 'Young people of minority ethnic origin in England and early parenthood: Views from young parents and service providers' in *Social Science and Medicine* 63: 858–870.

Hudson, F. & Ineichen, B. (1991). *Taking it Lying Down: Sexuality and Teenage Motherhood*. Basingstoke: Macmillan Publishing.

Inman, K. (2001). 'Pregnant Silence' *Guardian* 2.8.00. www.guardianunlimited.co.uk (accessed 2002).

Kalil, A., Ziol Guest, K. & Coley, R.L. (2005). 'Perceptions of father involvement patterns in teenage-mother families: Predictors and links to mothers' psycho-logical adjustment' in *Family Relations* 54 (2) April: 197–211.

Lamb, M.E. (1987). *The Father's Role: Cross Cultural Perspectives*. Hilsdale, New Jersey: Erlbaum.

Lamb, M.E. & Elster, A.B. (1985). 'Adolescent mother infant father relation-ships' in *Developmental Psychology* 21: 768–773.

Laub, J.H. & Sampson, R.J. (2003). *Shared Beginnings, Divergent Lives*. Cambridge MA: Harvard University Press.

Lloyd, T. & Forrest, S. (2001). *Boys and Young Men's Health: Literature and Practice Review*. Health Development Agency. Available online at www.hda-online.org.uk/documents/boyshealth (accessed 2003).

Lloyd, N., O'Brian, M. & Lewis, C. (2003). *Fathers in Sure Start Programmes*. Nottingham: Department for Education and Skills.

MacDonald, R. & Marsh, J. (2005). *Disconnected Youth? Growing Up in Britain's Poor Neighbourhoods*. Basingstoke: Palgrave Macmillan.

Oakely, A. (1979). *Becoming a Mother*. Oxford: Martin Robinson.

O'Brian, M. (2004). *Fathers and Family Support: Promoting Involvement and Evaluating Impact*. London: National Family and Parenting Institute.

O'Hagan, K. & Dillenberger, K. (1995). *The Abuse of Women within Child Care Work*. Buckingham: Open University Press.

Parke, R.D. (1996). *Fatherhood*. Cambridge MA: Harvard University Press.

Raneri, L. & Weinmann, C. (2007) Social Ecological Predictors of Repeat adolescent Pregnancy. *Sexual and Reproductive Health*. 39 (1):39–47

Reeves, J. (2003). *They should still be out playing: A contemporary analysis of young pregnant women/mothers in the care system*. Unpublished Thesis for Master of Philosophy in Social Work. University of Kent, Canterbury.

Reeves, J. (2006). *You've got to keep your head on: A study of the stories young men who are service users tell about the transition to fatherhood*. Unpublished PhD. Thesis, Open University.

Robb, M. (2007). 'Gender' in Kehily, M.J. (Ed.) *Understanding Youth: Perspectives, Identities and Practices*. London: Sage Publications:109–147.

Smith, P.B., Buzi, R.S., Weinman, M. & Mumford, D. (2001). 'The use of focus groups to identify needs and expectations of young fathers in male involvement program' in *Journal of Sex Education and Therapy* 26(2): 100–105.

Social Exclusion Unit (1998). *Bringing Britain Together: A National Strategy for Neighbourhood Renewal*. London: SEU.

Social Exclusion Unit (1999). *Teenage Pregnancy*. London: HMSO.

Social Exclusion Unit (2004). *Impact of the Teenage Pregnancy Strategy: Programme Report*. London: HMSO. www.dfes.gov.uk/teenagepregnancy (accessed 2005).

Stanley, N. (1997). 'Domestic violence and child abuse: Developing social work practice' in *Child and Family Social Work* 2: 135–145.

Sure Start Unit (2002). *Sure Start: A Guide to Planning and Running your Programme*. London: Sure Start Unit.

Tabberer, S., Hall, C., Prendergast, S. & Webster, A. (2000). *Teenage Pregnancy and Choice*. York: Joseph Rowntree Foundation

Tyrer, P., Chase, E., Warwick, I. & Aggleton, P. (2005). ' "Dealing with It" Experiences of young fathers in and leaving care' in *British Journal of Social Work* 35: 1107–1121.

Ward, L. (2002). 'Big increase pushes children up the agenda' in *The Guardian* 16 July: 11.

Weinmann, M.L., Smith, P.B. & Buzi, R. (2002). 'Young fathers: An analysis of risk behaviurs and service needs' in *Child and Adolescent Social Work Journal* 19(6): 437–453.

West, L. & Wenham, K. (2003). *A space for new stories? An interim Biographical Evaluation of Sure Start Millmead*. Canterbury: Christchurch University.

Williams, R.(1999). *Going the Distance: Fathers, Health and Health Visiting*. Reading: The University of Reading & The Queens Nursing Institute.

# Chapter 2
# The Legislative and Policy Context of Young Fathers and their Children

**Janet Webb**

## Introduction

'Family life should always be good. It should be a secure place where people love you.'

Dianna, aged 14 (Reeves 2003: 99)

In recent years there have been many legislative influences and policy changes that relate to children which also have a bearing on young fathers, who may themselves have the legal status of being a child as well as caring for one. Contemporary policy puts much emphasis on parenting and the support that might be needed to help families in bringing up children (Department for Education and Skills, DfES, 2004). It is recognised that parenting can be challenging (Gaskill 2006) and that, in the majority of cases, it should be the decision of parents when to ask for help and advice on their children's care and upbringing (HM Government 2006). Whilst it could be argued that parenting has become 'profession-alised' with a plethora of parenting programmes available to parents (Furedi 2002), it is also argued that professionals do need to engage with some parents early, especially when to do so may prevent problems or difficulties becoming worse (Quinton 2004). Young fathers are often the parents who are absent or non-resident and, indeed, are often vulnerable themselves (Chase *et al*. 2004, Hudson & Ineichen 1991, Reeves 2006). They are, therefore, likely to need support, as identified in recent policy documents (DfES 2003, 2004, HM Government 2004) and those professionals involved in working with them and their children should be cognisant of the legislation and policy guidance that influences their practice.

Moreover, it is well documented that it is in the child's best interest for professionals to engage with parents, working with them to enable them to become involved in the care of their children (Ghate & Hazel 2002, Howe 2005). This applies to young fathers as much as other parents. Whilst the focus is often with those families who are vulnerable, this shifting emphasis, which encompasses all fathers and their children, is seen as a positive development within the current Every Child Matters: Change for Children Agendas (DfES 2004). The focus of these agendas is that all children deserve the opportunity to achieve their full potential.

In the light of this, the focus of this chapter is to provide a review of key legislation, policy and recommendations, explain how they are interpreted and highlight the current issues in policy that pertain to young fathers and their children. The chapter will, firstly, discuss the legislation and policy context pertaining to fathers themselves and their children from a general perspective. Within this the focus will be on the best interests of the child, whether this be the fathers themselves or their children. Secondly, the focus will turn to human rights with the discussions picking up on some of the issues discussed in the preface to the book pertaining to definitions of young fathers and their children within the context of legislation. Following on from this, historical issues around fatherhood will  then be briefly considered. Finally, parental responsibility will be discussed within the context of the relevant legislative framework. However, in relation to this, it should be noted that the issue of consent is discussed in Chapter 3 in the context of the Fraser Rules. Discussion throughout this chapter will focus on legislation pertaining to the welfare of children from the Children Act 1989 to present day. It is within this context that young fathers are considered, as it is predominantly the same legislation that applies to both the young father and his child/children. Thus, the focus is child care legislation and policy from a generic perspective. The aspects of this legislation that specifically apply to safeguarding children are discussed later in this book in Chapter 4. This chapter sets the context for the book to enable the application of relevant legislation and policy in meeting the needs of both young fathers and their children.

# The legislative and policy context of young fathers

## Best Interests of the Child, Legislation and Policy

**Child's best interests**

It is sometimes difficult to differentiate between law, policy, and recommendations, as the imperative to abide by each and the penalties for failure to do so may seem equally stringent. Indeed, there are often no obvious practical differences between the three. As Rose (2007) notes, within all contemporary child care legislation, policies for practice and recommendations, the over-riding concern is for the welfare of the child. The imperative to make the right decision is not primarily in order to avoid penalty, but first and foremost, in order to provide the best possible care for children, young people and their families. The tension within the context of this book lies between meeting the needs of a young father, who may still be a child himself, and meeting the needs of his child, and ultimately acting in the best interests of both.

## Ethical Considerations

**Ethical considerations**

Ethics, or the study of right and wrong behaviour, is often used to justify difficult decisions (Rose 2007), particularly in terms of helping children and young people achieve positive outcomes as identified in current policy and legislation (DfES 2003). In this context, when considering working with young fathers and their offspring the following ethical principles apply:

- the best interests of the child (and young person)
- the promotion of personal autonomy
- the greatest good and least harm to the greatest number
- accountability for decisions made in the face of unclear or contradictory law, codes and recommendations.

The current overriding principle for children is that the child's (and young person's) welfare is paramount and that if there is a risk of harm or significant harm then the legislative framework of the Children Act 1989 applies and takes precedence over anything else (Parliament 1989). The two acts described below, the Children Act 1989 and the Children Act 2004 are the crucial Acts for those involved in working with children and young fathers regardless of whether they are employed in the statutory or voluntary sector (Johns 2005). Multi-agency and interdisciplinary working is also essential if outcomes for children and young people are to be achieved. The Common Core of Skills and Knowledge (2005) for the Children's Workforce is also important and sets out six areas of expertise that everyone working with children, young people and families should be able to demonstrate, notably inter-professional and interdisciplinary working and sharing information across agencies. This applies to meeting the needs of the young father and his child. Both may need intervention to ensure that firstly, the welfare and well-being of the father is upheld and secondly, that the young father is supported in meeting the needs of the child to prevent harm (issues about harm are discussed in Chapter 4).

## The Children Act 1989

**The Children Act 1989**

The Children Act 1989 applies in England and Wales, and is based on the principle outlined above that the child's welfare is paramount and that effective intervention should be in place to ensure the safety and well-being of children who are at risk of harm. It states that children should, wherever possible, be brought up and cared for within their own family, with both parents playing a full part in their lives, without resorting to legal proceedings. Only in situations where there is fundamental disagreement between parents, or concerns about a child's welfare, will the Courts make orders about a child's place of residence and contact arrangements. Aspects of this legislation that apply to safeguarding the welfare of children (and in some cases their fathers) will be discussed in more detail later in the chapter.

It is worth noting here that the developments of private law in the UK have assumed that continued contact with fathers is good for all children and that most fathers want contact (Lewis 2002). Indeed, this is addressed within the Children Act 1989, which regards disputes within families as falling under private law since the dispute is not between the family and the local authority. Relevant orders pertaining to this are found in Section 8 of the Children Act 1989 and these comprise four kinds (Johns 2005):

● residence orders which concern where children live

- contact orders which concern arrangements for children to keep in touch with others
- prohibited steps orders which stop someone doing something
- specific issue orders which compel someone to do something.

These orders are not exclusive to disputes within families and are sometimes used in care proceedings under public law provision of the Children Act 1989. The Children Act 1989 however, has a 'No Order' presumption, whereby there is an expectation that parents will come to their own agreements on issues affecting their children without the need of court proceedings. Situations do, however, occur in which a parent may have no other option than to apply to a court for an order. Even then, courts will encourage agreement and will only make an order if to do so would be better for the child than not doing so. Young fathers should, therefore, see a court application as a last resort when other options, including professional conciliation or mediation, have failed. The court may, in some instances, prevent further applications without the court's permission. However, in the case of young fathers disputes may occur if their relationship with the child's mother has broken down and it may be necessary to go to court in order for them to keep in touch with their child(ren).

Before making an order the court will in most cases direct that a welfare report be provided by the Court Welfare Service. Where issues of child protection are involved, a report from Social Services will be required. The orders are therefore applicable to young fathers when there is dispute between themselves and the biological mother of the child. If there are concerns around the child's welfare in relation to the mother, a resident order may be made for example for the child to live with the father and his parents (the paternal grandparents). In some circumstances children of young parents may live with the maternal grandparents and again the young father may need to apply for a contact order. A specific steps order may be used to compel the family to allow the young father to be involved in the care of his child if this is in the child's best interests. It is worth noting that the legislation in Scotland is different although the same principles apply.

## The Children (Scotland) Act 1995

**The Children (Scotland) Act 1995**

The Children (Scotland) Act 1995 applies in Scotland and is based on the following key principles:

- Each child has a right to be treated as an individual.
- Each child who can form his or her views on matters affecting him or her has the right to express those views if he or she wishes.
- Parents should normally be responsible for the upbringing of their child and should share that responsibility.
- Each child has the right to protection from all forms of abuse, neglect or exploitation.
- In decisions relating to the protection of a child, every effort should be made to keep the child in the family home.
- Any intervention by a public authority in the life of a child should be properly supported by services from all relevant agencies working in collaboration.

## The Children Act 2004

**The Children Act 2004**

The Children Act 2004 gives a focus and status to children's services, strengthening but not replacing existing legislation. The Green Paper 'Every Child Matters' proposed changes in policy and legislation in England to maximise opportunities and minimise risks for all children and young people, focusing services more effectively around the needs of children, young people and their families. The Act gives effect to the legislative proposals set out in the Green Paper to create clear accountability for children's services, to enable better joint working and to secure a better focus on safeguarding children (Webb 2007).

### Key components of the Act

The Children Act 2004 is the legislative spine of the current reforms of children's (and young people's services), and has established:

- a Children's Commissioner to champion the views and interests of children and young people;

- a duty on Local Authorities to make arrangements to promote co-operation between agencies and other appropriate bodies (such as voluntary and community organisations) in order to improve children's well-being (where well-being is defined by reference to the five outcomes), and a duty on key partners to take part in the co-operation arrangements;

- a duty on key agencies to safeguard and promote the welfare of children;

- a duty on Local Authorities to set up Local Safeguarding Children Boards and on key partners to take part (these replace Area/Local Child Protection Committees or ACPC/LCPCs);

- the provision of indexes or databases containing basic information about children and young people to enable better sharing of information;

- a requirement for a single Children and Young People's Plan to be drawn up by each Local Authority;

- a requirement on Local Authorities to appoint a Director of Children's Services and designate a Lead Member;

- the creation of an integrated inspection framework and the conduct of Joint Area Reviews to assess local areas' progress in improving outcomes; and

- provisions relating to foster care, private fostering and the education of children in care.

## The National Service Framework for Children, Young People and Maternity Services (NSF)

**National Service Framework**

**This is underpinned by the Children Act 2004 in which there is a refusal to separate child protection from wider policies to improve children's lives.** The NSF appears to be building on the underlying philosophy of the Children Act 1989 as well as the recommendations from both the Kennedy and Laming inquiries in that the children's welfare is paramount. It sets a ten year strategy and suggests standards for the first time for children's health and social care. In the context of thinking about young fathers it is Standard 5 which has particular relevance as it is concerned with safeguarding and promoting the welfare of children. It requires that: 'All agencies work together to prevent children suffering harm and to promote their welfare, provide them with services they require to address their identified needs and safeguard children who are being or who are likely to be harmed' (DH 2004b: 6).

## Contemporary Context: Every Child (and Young Person) Matters

**Every Child Matters**

It was in response to the enquiry into the high profile case of the death of Victoria Climbié (Laming 2003), that the government published the Green Paper: *Every Child Matters: Change for Children* (Department for Education and Skills, DfES, 2003). The report set the agenda for far reaching structural changes to the delivery of all services to children, young people and families and work force reform. The Change for Children programme demands a radical transformation of services through new structures, a reframing of how children, young people and families receive universal services and an integration of targeted and specialist services. Additionally, a unique step has been taken in defining specific outcomes for all children and young people with the result that all services will be measured against five core outcomes. These outcomes are seen as being key to children's and young people's wellbeing. The five core outcomes are:

- Being healthy: enjoying good physical and mental health and living a healthy lifestyle;
- Staying safe: being protected from harm and abuse;
- Enjoying and achieving: getting the most out of life and developing skills for adulthood;
- Making a positive contribution: being involved with the community and society and not engaging in anti-social or offending behaviour;
- Achieving economic well-being: not being prevented by economic disadvantage from achieving their full potential in life.

The aim of these outcomes is to ensure that every child and young person has the chance to fulfil their potential. They are central to the current programme of change (DfES, 2004) and are at the heart of the reforms set out in the Children Act (2004). The rationale for this large-scale reform agenda is both to 'protect children and maximise their potential' (DfES, Every Child Matters: Change for Children, 2003: 5). Within this context child protection is now recognised as being 'everyone's responsibility' and this concept will be returned to later in Chapter 4.

The Children Act 2004 is the cornerstone for the reorganisation of services to children, young people and their families and it ring fences the Every Child Matters Agendas. This Act affirms that all children (and young people) come under the purview of the state and in doing so it has created a hierarchical model as a way of locating those in greatest need within the context of all children and their universal needs and services (Horner & Krawczyk, 2006). Young fathers and their children are often those in greatest need and the need to address their vulnerabilities to improve their lives is explicitly acknowledged within this contemporary policy.

## Recent developments

**Recent developments**

It is acknowledged that young people have different needs to children but that all ages from 0 to 19 years should be facilitated to achieve the five Every Child Matters outcomes.

Following on from Every Child Matters, Youth Matters, the Youth Green Paper, was published on 18 July 2005. The subsequent consultation had over 19,000 responses from young people themselves.

The government response, Youth Matters: Next Steps (DfES 2005, DCSF 2007) was published on 8 March 2006 and sets out the vision for empowering young people, giving them somewhere to go, something to do and someone to talk to. It is intended that young people will have more choice and influence over services and facilities that are available to them.

## Applying the outcomes to young fathers

Thus, the five core outcomes identified above are particularly significant within the context of young fathers. However, if the young father is under 18 years of age he is legally a child himself. At this point it is worth pointing out that the Children Act 1989

(Parliament 1989) defines a child as someone who has not yet reached their 18th birthday. The Every Child Matters policies however, address the needs of young people up to the age of 19 years. Whilst at 19 they are legally an adult the policy is in place to help ensure smoother transitions to adulthood and to adult services if required.

It is important to note that if the father is below 19 years of age the five Every Child Matters outcomes apply both to the father and their child and consequently professionals have a dual responsibility to both parties. If the young father is not in education or employment interventions are required that will help him achieve the outcomes in order to help him make the transition to adulthood. Tensions often arise, however, when the young person becomes an adult. The interface between child and adult services often does not always match up. Furthermore, children of vulnerable young fathers are vulnerable themselves. Professionals have a responsibility to intervene and prevent the vulnerabilities becoming worse. Early intervention and prevention is a key philosophy of current policy agendas (DfES 2004). Early intervention services are integral to the reform of children's services as is the need to work together and share information.

---

### Good Practice Box

Those working with children of young fathers who have reached their 18th birthday need to ensure that they liaise and work with other professionals and the services in place to meet the needs of the father. The sharing of information across both child and adult services is essential to ensure that the welfare of the child is protected.

---

### The Common Assessment Framework

**The Common Assessment Framework**

In relation to the above, the Common Assessment Framework is being introduced nationally (DfES 2006). It is an assessment format that can be used by a range of professionals in assessing the needs of a child, leading, where a multi-agency approach is needed, to the selection of a lead professional to work with the family to coordinate services' responses to that assessed need. A young father and his child may both need to be assessed. However, if the father is non-resident and vulnerable or in need of intervention himself the assessment may well be carried out by different agencies. Information sharing is thus crucial and is addressed in the Children Act 2004 (HM Government 2004) which places a duty on local authorities to make arrangements through which key agencies co-operate to improve the well-being of children and young people. Additionally, safeguarding children continues to be given priority as the Act places a responsibility for key agencies to have regard to the need to safeguard children and promote their welfare in exercising their normal functions. Specific issues around safeguarding children and young people will be addressed in Chapter 4.

## Contact Point

**Contact Point**

To support professionals in working together and sharing information to identify difficulties and provide appropriate support, the Children Act 2004 requires the creation of a national database to hold information on all children and young people (Section 12). This UK national children's services database will be known as Contact Point. Ultimately the records representing the approximately 12.3 m children across England from birth to the age of 18 will be linked together within Contact Point. This data base is a key element of the government's 'Every Child Matters: Change for Children Agendas' to support more effective delivery of children's services in England through better sharing of information among authorised users in children and young people's services.

Contact Point is intended to provide a secure and efficient way to find out who else is working with the same child or young person, making it easier to deliver co-ordinated support. The system will for each child or young person index information including: name, address, gender, date of birth and a unique identifying number, together with basic identification information about a child's parent or carer.

Additional information and details will held on contact in relation to services involved with the child such as their school, GP practice and other services. These will include the name of the lead practitioner and whether an assessment has been undertaken under the Common Assessment Framework. However, access to the system will be restricted to authorised workers/professionals who need it as part of their job or role and who have been security-checked, trained and have the necessary authentication.

## 'Looked after' young fathers

**'Looked after' young fathers**

It is also worth noting that the Children Act 2004 (HM Government 2004) creates a new duty for local authorities to promote the educational achievement of looked after children and an associated power to transmit data relating to individual children in monitoring this (Sections 52 and 54). This may well apply to the child and the young father. In relation to this it is also important to be aware that the Children (Leaving Care) Act 2000 focuses on the needs of young people 16–17 years of age who were looked after by the local authority. It gives a local authority the duty to provide a personal advisor and prepare a pathway plan for them as they make the transition to adulthood and possibly adult services. Support and material assistance can be offered until the age of 21. If the young person is a father wishing to engage with his child, this would also need to be taken into account in terms of support and in terms of contact with the child if the father is non-resident. The pathway plan should be multi-agency and include contributions from children's services with respect to the young father's child. This should enable professionals to support young fathers in a more co-ordinated way

There is an overall focus in the Children Act 2004 on an integrated front line delivery with the belief that more integrated children's services will mean children and young people, including young fathers themselves, will:

- be safeguarded from harm;
- have better opportunities to develop and reach their full potential;
- receive effective support earlier if they experience difficulties; and
- be better able to access targeted services faster and with less stigma as a result of closer links between these targeted services and universal services.

# The legislative and policy context of young fathers

Parents, including those who are young fathers, should therefore have:

- more information advice and support
- access to targeted support when needed.

## Case Scenario

John was 15 when his baby was born. He faced negativity from his girlfriend and his girlfriend's parents. He was not fully engaged in education at the time of the baby's birth.

John himself is one of six. Two of his brothers are autistic. His mother had him when she was in care, aged 15. John has never known his father and a stepfather left a while ago. Small but strong, he was bullied and fought back. Deemed out of control, he was excluded from school. The school however, referred him to a learning mentor who works with school aged fathers. His learning mentor provided in depth support and liaised with both John's family and his girlfriend's family. John wanted to be involved with his baby but needed additional support to enable this to happen. Barriers to education were removed and John was empowered to be involved. His mentor liaised with his girlfriend and her family and helped to change their attitudes and they began to see how important it was for John to be involved with the baby.

John's mentor works in a team which offers young dads whatever help they need to improve their prospects – both in terms of their education, future career, and of their role as a parent. A range of parenting training is available from the team's specialist nursery nurses. The team gave John respect and empowered him, thus helping him to get back 'on track' and make the transition to parenthood and also on track to achieve.

Young fathers often face many adversities and are often not fully engaged with education. Furthermore, the stereotype of a teenage dad is that of a 'feckless youth' who runs away the moment the pregnancy test strip turns blue, if not before. However, in reality many young fathers want to be involved but often they need additional support to do this, especially in the early stages (Fathers Direct 2007). Young fathers also often face negativity from the mothers, family, and sometimes from the mother and even from their own parents and peer group, as well as from some professionals. It is however, important that professionals work together and recognise that young fathers have a right to be given 'the chance' (Fathers Direct 2007).

Young fathers, however, are in the complex position of making the transition to adulthood and therefore crucially have rights both as young people as well as parents. Interventions and services, therefore, need to be coordinated and integrated and the trajectories of these young people's lives and the assessment of their needs as fathers need to addressed. Thus social support may be required for the young father as well as the child. This is particularly relevant if the young father is involved in the criminal justice system as in the case of Jay below.

## Case Scenario

Jay is 18 years of age. He has lived in Youth Custody. He has no contact with his own family parents or siblings. His baby is 6 months old. He intends to live with his partner and their baby as he feels that this will make him change his lifestyle. However, he has expressed feelings of not being able to cope with the constant crying of the baby. He has limited support himself although the maternal grandparents have become involved recently, although they have only been reunited with their 18-year-old daughter within the last two months. As Jay says 'Hazel wasn't in contact with her parents until social services told her we can take him away or you go and stay with your parents . . . last they knew their daughter was 17 and living in a hostel and now she is 18 and has a baby and partner'.

- Clearly if Jay is to remain involved with his baby and partner he needs encouragement and support.
- His social worker and probation officer need to communicate with those involved in his partner's and baby's lives.
- A multi-agency plan of intervention is required. If various agencies are all working independently this could lead to confusion.
- Jay has a right to be a father. His name is on the birth certificate. However, with rights come responsibilities and he is going to need support in order to fulfil his responsibilities and he should be afforded respect as a father to the baby.

## Connexions

**Connexions**

It is worth mentioning here the government youth agency 'Connexions' which was established in 2002 as a means of tackling social exclusion among young people. Its aim is to assist young people make a transition to adulthood. Connexions is the government's support service for all young people aged 13 to 19 in England. It also provides support up to the age of 25 for young people who have learning difficulties or disabilities (or both).

Through multi-agency working, Connexions provides information, advice, guidance and access to personal development opportunities for young people. It aims to remove barriers to learning and progression, and ensure young people make a smooth transition to adulthood and working life.

## Young Person: the Concept

**'Young Person'**

There are various definitions of 'young people' within UK policy and legislation demonstrating variations that occur in relation to what is perceived to constitute young and youth. A young person in Britain is generally defined as a person between 14 and 19 years of age. Health and safety law defines a young person as anyone under 18 years of age (Health and Safety Executive 2007). For the purposes of unemployment benefit a distinction is made between under 25s and those over 25, with the latter group considered to be adults. This categorisation came into being in October 1996, reducing actual benefit amount for those under 25, thus having implications for those supporting children including young fathers. The Social Exclusion Unit within the Office of the Deputy Prime Minister refers to the age group 16–25 as 'young adults', although the department responsible for tackling homelessness refers to this age group as 'young people'. Within the legislative framework of the Children Act 1989 a 'child' is defined as anyone under the age of 18. Clearly there are discrepancies which could be confusing between agencies when trying to put services in place to support young fathers and afford them their rights.

## Rights and legislation

## Rights and legislation

Often a number of important ethical and legal issues arise in relation to the issue of rights which are applicable to young fathers and their families (Johns 2005). For example, to what extent should the state intervene in the lives of people who may not have committed a crime, yet may potentially pose a threat in terms of harming others, including their children or are vulnerable themselves, as in the case of Jay? There are, however, conventions and bench marks established under the auspices of the United Nations against which countries can be assessed on compliance with basic human rights (Johns 2005).

Under both domestic and international law it is uncontested that children have a right to be protected from harm and to have their basic physical and social needs met. Historically this has been the focus of concern. More recently however, there has been a shift in attitude toward children's (and now young people's) rights and it is now acknowledged that they are holders of rights associated with expressing their views and participating in the making of decisions which affect them directly. This shift in emphasis was initially reflected in the principles of the Children Act 1989 which provides for children's views to be heard and to be given due consideration by courts and other bodies responsible for deciding on matters, such as residence and contact between children and non-resident parents. Nonetheless, children's rights are restricted by two important considerations:

- firstly, their best interests
- secondly, the question of whether children have the mental capacity to exercise their rights responsibly and make an informed choice or decision.

Professionals often find it difficult to achieve a balance between these two principles. International law provides useful guidance in this context.

The United Nations Convention on the Rights of the Child 1989 (UNCRC), was ratified by the United Kingdom (UK) in 1991. It establishes a range of rights for children (and young people) from social, economic, cultural, civil and political perspectives. It also provides that children's best interests are to be a primary consideration for policy and decision makers and that the evolving capacity of children must also be taken into consideration in law and policy. Professionals must therefore be cognisant with this and recognise that children and young people, and therefore young fathers, have specific rights that include:

- the right to protection
- the right to participate and to have your say
- the right to a family life
- the right to have decisions that affect you made in your best interests
- the right to be involved in making those decisions.

## The Human Rights Act 1998

**The Human Rights Act 1998**

In addition to child specific law, the Human Rights Act (1998) also addresses these issues and provides the bench mark for young fathers both as a parent and a child. All need to be taken into account when planning services and interventions for young fathers.

The Human Rights Act 1998 which became law in 2000 underpins all UK law related to the functioning of public authorities such as the NHS and local authorities. It was designed to protect individuals from the power of the state. It also requires that public bodies such as local authorities act in accordance with the Convention on Human Rights and offers a way of challenge if they do not (Jowitt & O'Loughlin 2005).

Many rights are set out in the Act but of particular importance to those working with young fathers and their children are the following:

- the right to life: Article 2
- the right not to be subjected to degrading treatment: Article 3
- the right to respect private and family life: Article 6
- the right not to suffer discrimination in relation to any of the other basic rights: Article 14.

(Glasper & Mitchell 2005)

The Human Rights Act 1998 is central to the right of self-determination by children and young people and includes their right to consent or refuse treatment (Lowden 2002). The Children Act 1989 and the Children (Scotland) Act 1995 however, whilst providing legislation that relates to the care and treatment of children and their upbringing and protection from harm, does not go beyond establishing their right to be involved in decision making about their welfare. The Human Rights Act 1998 enables action to be taken if it is proved that children's rights have been infringed. Furthermore, the Children Act 2004 strengthens this and places a new duty on local authorities. Before determining what (if any) services to provide under Section 17 of the Children Act 1989 for a particular child in need, local authorities have to ascertain the child's wishes and feelings regarding the provision of those services, and give due consideration to them (Section 53). Thus children should be involved in the decision making process about what happens to them and, in the case of young fathers, their children. Decisions about the children are clearly within the context of young father and the child's mother cooperating to keep them free from harm.

Article 8 (2) of the Human Rights Act 1998 states that there shall be no interference with the exercise of the right to privacy, family life, home and correspondence except such as is in accordance with the law and is necessary in a democratic society in the interests of national security, public safety or the economic well-being of the country, for the prevention of disorder or crime, for the protection of health or morals, or for the protection of the rights and freedom of others (Children Act Section 3 (1)). Thus if a child was being 'harmed' the Children Act 1989 or the Children (Scotland) Act 1995 would override the decision making process in the best interests of the child (Johns 2005).

## Needs, responsibilities and rights

**Needs, responsibilities and rights**

With rights come societal responsibilities and subsequently new challenges for those working with children, young people and their families in any setting. In the past children were considered to be individuals with needs, whereas in contemporary society they are considered to be individuals with rights (Glasper & Mitchell 2005). In relation to children in this context the United Nations Convention on the Rights of the Child (1989) applies

(United Nations General Assembly 1989). This sets out the basic human rights that all children are entitled to without discrimination. The convention is underpinned by four guiding principles:

- non-discrimination (Article 2)
- the best interests of the child (Article 3), which may also apply to the father as well as his child
- survival and development (Article 6)
- participation (Article 12).

The British Government ratified the document in 1991 and by doing so committed itself to protecting and ensuring children's rights and agreed to hold itself accountable before the international community. Although in itself it is not a legal statute, the United Nations Convention on the Rights of the Child can be used to support the rights of children, under the age of 18 years. Legislation which builds on the articles contained in the Convention on the Rights of the Child, seeks to offer further protection to one of the most vulnerable groups within society (Glasper & Mitchell 2005).

## Policy perspectives on fatherhood

**Policy perspectives**

It is worth commenting that some aspects of fatherhood have had a 'bad press' in Britain over the last few years. Public discussion has focused, in particular, on the growing numbers of fathers who live apart from their, often young, children, many of whom play a marginal role in their children's lives, financially, socially and emotionally (Burghes *et al.* 1997) and these issues are addressed later in depth in Chapters 5 and 6. As Lewis (2002) notes, fathers of all ages did not enter the public policy agenda in Britain until the end of the 1980s as prior to this time they were eclipsed by debates on lone mothers (Carabine 2001). Historically Britain has constructed the role of the father as 'bread winner' and there has been continued emphasis on the father to maintain (Lewis 2002). Fathers have been perceived as being marginal in terms of 'hands on' child care. However, fathers became the focus of policy agendas in the 1980s when they were seen as being increasingly absent and their failure to maintain was putting a burden on the social security budget. Keeping fathers attached to their families and enforcing parental responsibility became significant issues.

# Inter-professional approaches to young fathers

The Matrimonial and Family Proceedings Act, passed in 1984, contained a number of provisions designed to direct the court's attention to the principle of 'self-sufficiency' and to facilitate, in appropriate cases, the making of a 'clean break' between husbands and wives (Davis *et al.* 1994). The implication of this legislation was that men were being freed from lifelong obligations to their first families from both a monetary and social perspective (Davis *et al.* 1994). However, the rapid increase in lone families in the 1980s and the concomitant rise in the cost of supporting (mainly) mothers and children by the state, generated debate about what fatherhood meant and what a father should be or should do (Lewis 2002).

The Child Support Act 1991 required all fathers who were divorced and unmarried to support their biological children regardless of their social arrangements. This legislation has been interpreted as an attempt to reinforce the 'male breadwinner' model family in the absence of a stable marriage in that it also contained an element of support for mothers.

The 1984 legislation had overturned the notion of a father's persistent obligation to pay spousal maintenance. However, the 1991 legislation justified maintenance for the mothers in terms of the mother being unable to enter the labour market because of her caring role (Maclean 1994).

Thus, through the 1991 legislation the state enforced the obligations of fathers in terms of their biological responsibilities to their children. However, problems arose in relation to how the 1991 legislation was implemented and interpreted Lewis (2002). Child support legislation appeared to perpetuate the traditional gender roles of mothers and fathers beyond the point of relationship breakdown, without addressing the need for non-resident fathers to provide care. The implication of this for young fathers was to potentially further exclude them as a group, labelling them as 'bad dads', as they are often not in a position to provide financial support and also not encouraged to provide care.

Some would argue that financial support should be concomitant with right of access to the child thus providing opportunity to care for the child. Thus, if a man of any age cannot provide financial support then they cannot provide care. Care is therefore seen as subordinate to financial support for the child and portrayed as a luxury and as in the interests of the father, as opposed to the best interests of the child. Furthermore, the care support policy of the 1991 legislation relied on the existence of a family wage, which in the case of young fathers, who as a group are more likely to be excluded and have few educational qualifications (SEU 1999), might not be the case. Furthermore, if breadwinning is still a key component of modern fatherhood, how possible is it for young men to take on the social and legal status of being a father if they have no jobs and poor economic prospects? Thus, whilst the economic underpinning of fatherhood should not be ignored, fatherhood is more than just the financial support of families (Burghes *et al.* 1997), especially in the case of young fathers who may not be in a position to provide financial support.

## Recent approaches

In recent years, policy regarding fathers and care has been substantially revised, explicitly addressing both the issue of child poverty and reconciling both family and workplace responsibilities from both the mother's and father's perspective. As Jowett and O'Loughlin (2005) note, this implies a shift in thinking about the position of children in our society, from being the sole responsibility of their parents to one of social investment thereby ensuring the future stability of society (Featherstone 2004, Frost 2003). The issue of child care is now located within the wider context of supporting families in parenting more generally (DfES 2003). The Children Act 1989 was pivotal to this perspective with its emphasis on parental responsibility and partnership with parents and professionals in resolving concerns about children. Furthermore, the maintenance of family links is central to the Children Act 1989 and where a child is cared for by a local authority the biological parents still retain their parental responsibility (Jowett & O'Loughlin 2005).

## Fatherhood and parental responsibility

**Parental responsibility**

The basic premise of the Children Act 1989 is that children's wellbeing is best promoted by encouraging and supporting them to live with their own families (Johns 2005). There are situations however, where professionals are required to intervene in a family's life if there are concerns about a child's welfare. However, before discussing this, it is important to consider the notion of parental responsibility and to note that there is a distinction between parenthood, parenting and parental responsibility.

Parental responsibility is defined in Section 3(1) of the Children Act 1989 as 'all the rights, duties, powers, responsibilities and authority which, by law, a parent has in relation to a child and his property'. It is the people with parental responsibility who have the legal authority with respect to their child; they are the decision makers who must be consulted (Johns 2005).

It is important to realise that for children in public care their parents retain parental responsibility, either:

- sharing it with the local authority, in the case of those on Care Orders; or

- entirely, in the case of those 'accommodated' under Section 20 of the Children Act 1989.

Parents continue to have parental responsibility for their child, even when they are no longer living with them. Importantly parents should be kept informed about their children and participate in decisions made about their child's future

It is important to note that young fathers can have parental responsibility even if they themselves are defined as a child by the Children Act 1989.

## Case Scenario

Jane, aged 3 years, was fostered at birth under a care order. Susan and Rory, her parents, both aged 16 at the time, were unable to meet Jane's needs and had no support from their own families. At the time Susan was insistent that she would be able to care for her baby. However, because of concerns over Susan's and her partner's ability to meet Jane's needs a care order was applied for and granted by the courts.

Susan and Rory both share parental responsibility with the local authority. They were not married but Rory's name is on Jane's birth certificate. Susan's social worker acts on behalf of the local authority. However, Susan and Rory must both be consulted and be involved in decisions about Jane, such as, which school Jane might go to.

## Possible complexities for young fathers:
## Parenthood, duties and responsibilities

**Complexities**

There are differences between parenthood and parenting and thus an implied difference between fatherhood and being a father, although legislation pertaining to the welfare of children does not distinguish between genders. It is 'parents' who have responsibilities, as enshrined in the Children Act 1989 (Parliament 1989). As Johns (2005) notes, parenthood itself is generally understood to refer to both motherhood and fatherhood and is therefore equated with those people who are the biological parents of children. However, the law does not use the term 'parenthood', thus both motherhood and fatherhood are concepts rather than a legal status. The law does, however, concern itself with parental responsibility and this includes defining who has this (mother, father, another or state). The law is also very clear that there is a difference between parental duties and parental responsibility. Those who have parental responsibility clearly have obligations to the child, and the law tends to focus on these obligations as being primarily financial, a duty to maintain, enforced, if necessary by child support legislation as discussed above (Johns 2005). Thus parental duty pertains to financial support which, as previously raised, may be difficult for a young father not in employment.

Parenting implies a process whereby a particular kind of nurturing and development is provided for children (Johns 2005). This 'involves caring for a child's basic needs, keeping them safe, showing them warmth and love, providing the stimulation needed for their development and to help them achieve their potential' (HM Government 2006: 31). As such, this kind of upbringing does not have to be provided by biological parents. Johns (2005) comments that within the framework of current legislation the people who are the child's mother and father are not automatically people with parental responsibility for the child. They are though automatically people with parental duties. If the mother and father are married at the time of the child's birth then they do both share parental responsibility automatically (Section 2, Children Act 1989). The regulations on parental responsibility can be summarised as follows:

- If the parents are not married, the mother automatically has parental responsibility, as does the father if his name is registered on the birth certificate (Section 111, Adoption and Children Act 2002).

- Additionally, even if the father's name was not registered, it is possible for him to acquire parental responsibility either by marrying, by making a parental responsibility agreement, or by a court order known as a parental responsibility order (Section 4, Children Act 1989).

- It should be highlighted that parental responsibility is not exclusively limited to the parents (Johns 2005). Other people such as grandparents or step parents might acquire parental responsibility by becoming the child's guardian or by being granted a residence order by the court (as discussed below).

- If children are committed to care under a care order, local authorities also acquire parental responsibility and in this case their right to determine where the child should live overrides that of the parents (Section 33, Children Act 1989).

- Furthermore, a young father under the age of 16 years may also be being looked after by people other than his own biological parents. In such a case contact with his own child should be facilitated and he should still be consulted in terms of his own child.

Parental responsibility covers parental rights in relation to making decisions about children, such as deciding where a child should live, where they should go to school and how their other welfare needs should be met. As White *et al.* (2002) note, this pertains to protection, discipline, medical treatment, religion, property, amongst other decisions. It is in this context, therefore, that the term 'Good Enough Parenting' is often referred to. This term is often used to imply acceptable levels of parenting or child care that helps to ensure that the health, safety and developmental needs of children are met and refers to the provision of care and control (Powell & Ireland 2006). Care involves anticipating children's age-appropriate needs through pre-natal care, adequate feeding, warmth and protection from harm. Young people who have children and are cohabiting may well support each other in making these decisions, but unless they have parental responsibility then they cannot, for example, give consent for medical treatment.

## Implications for young fathers

## Implications for fathers

This legislation and policy clearly has implications for young fathers. If they wish to be involved in the care and not just have financial obligations, they need to ensure that they acquire parental responsibility even if they are not resident fathers. Non-resident fathers can share parental responsibility with the mother and this needs to be considered by those working with young fathers and their families. It is also important to remember that non-resident fathers who have parental responsibility should be consulted and involved in decisions about the care of their child. Parental responsibility also refers to status to participate in legal proceedings which again has implications for young fathers who themselves may require an advocate in court should there be a dispute as to who cares for the child or who the child lives with.

---

### Parental responsibility – Key Points

- Parental responsibility is defined as, 'All the rights, duties, powers, responsibilities and authority which a parent has in relation to the child and the child's property.'
- Birth mothers (and fathers married to the birth mother) automatically have parental responsibility.
- Fathers who are not married to the mother at the time of the birth but who have their name on the birth certificate have parental responsibility.
- The natural father who is not married to the birth mother can acquire parental responsibility by means of a formal agreement with the mother or on application to Court for an order granting parental responsibility or on the grant of a Residence Order. Parental responsibility in these circumstances can be terminated by Court Order.
- Parental responsibility may be acquired by other adults in the child's life through a Court Order but will cease when the Order ends or is terminated.
- Parents with parental responsibility can appoint a Guardian to have parental responsibility upon death of the parent.
- The local authority will acquire parental responsibility upon

---

the granting of a Care Order. Limited responsibility is given with an Emergency Protection Order.

● Under Adoption Orders, parental responsibility lies solely with the adopters.

● Parental responsibility may be acquired by more than one person through the courts.

## How do young fathers acquire parental responsibility?

There are five ways:

**A. The first is to have the father's name put on the birth certificate** when they register the birth of their child (if the child was born after 1 December 2003). This requires the mother's consent (and if the mother does not consent, they will need to go for a Parental Responsibility Order through the courts – see 'D' below).

**B. The second way is to re-register the birth**, and have the father's name put on the birth certificate this time

**C. The third way is for the father to marry the mother of their child.** They can be married at the time they register the birth or can marry afterwards. However, if they were not married at the time of their child's birth, and the father's name is not on the birth certificate, the father will need to make sure that, as well as marrying the child's mother, his name is put on the birth certificate (advice would be to consult a solicitor).

**D. The fourth way is by both the father and the mother of their child signing what is known as a 'Parental Responsibility Agreement' (PRA).**

They have to get this signed with witnesses.

**E. The fifth way** is to get parental responsibility without the agreement or willingness of the child's mother and this **is called a Parental Responsibility Order** (because a Judge 'orders' it in the face of her opposition).

To obtain a Parental Responsibility Order the father must seek it from their local County Court. They will need a solicitor.

# The legislative and policy context of young fathers

It is worth noting that there may be disputes within families, especially if the young father is no longer in a relationship with the mother and this is worth considering here within the context of legislation. Should there be a dispute within a family as to whom the child lives with it may be necessary to settle this within the courts. Cases such as this are regarded as 'private' law cases, since the dispute is within the family and not between the family and the local authority (Johns 2005). If there were child protection concerns, the local authority may well apply to the courts for an order to determine where the child should be cared for and this is a matter of public law. However, in the case of 'private' law the relevant orders are found in Section 8 Children Act 1989 (see above). The orders however, are not exclusive to child protection procedures and may be appropriate in care proceedings as part of child protection processes as an alternative to care orders or supervision orders. Certain categories of people can make an application for a residence or contact order under Section 8, Children Act 1989 and these include:

- the parent or guardian of a child
- anyone who holds a residence order in respect of that child
- a married step parent of the child where the child lived with the step parent as a child of the family
- anyone with whom the child has lived for at least 3 years (this period need not have been continuous but must have been recent)
- anyone:
  a) where there is already a residence order in place and who has the consent of every one who holds that order, or
  b) who has the consent of the local authority where the child is in their care or
  c) has the consent of every one who has parental responsibility for the child.

If an applicant cannot apply for the order as of right they can make an application to the court seeking leave to issue the application. In deciding whether to grant the leave the court will consider, amongst other things:

- the nature of the application
- the applicant's connection with the child

- the risk there might be of the proposed application disrupting the child's life to such an extent that they should be harmed by it.

It is via this route that wider family members such as grandparents are able to seek orders in respect of their grandchildren. In the case of young fathers it is often the grandparents who are involved in the care of the child and if the grandparent is going to care for a child on a long-term basis a residence order may be advisable as it:

- secures the long-term future of the child
- clarifies the grandparent's rights and responsibilities.

## Case Scenario

Julie and her partner Frank, both aged 18 are the parents of a two-year-old girl, Lucy. Lucy has lived with Julie's parents since birth because neither Julie nor Frank were able to cope. Julie and Frank are now living together in a flat and feel as though they have got themselves 'together' and feel able to look after themselves and Lucy. Julie's parents are arguing that Julie and Frank gave up their parental rights because Julie signed a letter saying they could take care of her.

However, Julie's and Frank's signatures only demonstrated their feelings at the time of the agreement and the letter is not a legally binding document. Since Julie's parents do not have *parental responsibility*, Julie and Frank may legally remove Lucy from their care. It is however, best to do this with as little disruption to Lucy as possible. It seems likely that Julie's parents will object to this, so they may wish to consider appointing a solicitor to contact Julie's parents on their behalf. They could also consider applying to court for a *residence order*. The advice would be to act in the best interests of Lucy and bear in mind that this difficult scenario may upset her.

Julie's parents could also apply for a residence order.

It is worth noting the effect of residence orders. These do not divest other parents of their parental duties and responsibilities but they do give the person with the residence order the right to say where the child will live and make decisions about them. If a young father, not married to the mother and not otherwise entitled to parental responsibility, is awarded a residence order, he is automatically awarded a separate parental responsibility order (Section 12, Children Act 1989). Residence orders do not allow a name change or change of identity for the child, nor do they allow the child to live abroad, except with the permission of everyone who has parental responsibility.

---

**Good Practice Box**

**Think about the legal implications for young fathers you are working with**

Young fathers may not fully understand their legal position regarding parental responsibility.

Do they need to acquire the responsibilities as described above?

Some young men live with children they are not biological fathers to because of their relationship with a partner.

Unless the young man has acquired parental responsibility as described above then they have no legal grounds for making decisions about the children of their partner even if they are cohabiting.

---

## Conclusions

This chapter has provided an overview of the policy and legislation that applies to young fathers and their children. It has done this from a generic perspective and the application to children and young people has been highlighted. The legislative framework for young fathers is the same as for children in relation to ensuring that their welfare is protected and their well-being maintained. Policy agendas apply key themes to both children and their young fathers. The discussions have addressed the key legislation in terms of the Children Act 1989 and the Children Act 2004. The issues of human rights and parental responsibility have also been discussed.

The area of child and family law and policy is complex and this chapter has provided an overview of contemporary policy relating to children from the Children Act 1989 to present day, providing insight into the aspects of legislation and policy that are relevant to those providing services for young fathers and their children. It has shown how the focus of work has changed and is changing. The Children Act 1989 and the Children Act 2004 are the crucial Acts for those involved in working with children and their fathers regardless of whether they are employed in the statutory or voluntary sector (Johns 2005).

Contemporary policy is embedded within the Every Child and Youth Matters Programmes for children and young people. Policy regarding fathers and care has been substantially revised in recent years and there is a shift in thinking about the position of children and young people in our society. They are no longer the sole responsibility of their parents but of society as a whole. In this context professionals represent society in ensuring that all children and young people have the opportunity to achieve the Every Child Matters outcomes. Additionally, the issue of child care is now located within the wider context of supporting families in parenting more generally (DfES 2003). The Children Act 1989 was pivotal to this perspective with its emphasis on parental responsibility and partnership with parents and professionals in resolving concerns about children. Furthermore, the maintenance of family links is central to the Children Act 1989 and where a child is cared for by a local authority the biological parents still retain their parental responsibility (Jowett & O'Loughlin 2005). Provision has been made within policy to facilitate young fathers engaging in the care of their children, which is seen as a positive move towards helping all children achieve.

## Key Messages

- There is no doubt that policy has begun to capture dimensions of fathering through legislation like the Child Support Act, 1991 and the Criminal Justice Act, 1991 and with the more recent reforms as part of the Every Child and Youth Matters agendas (DfES 2006, Department for Children, Schools and Families 2007).
- Fathers matter and society as a whole benefits from good fathering (Fathers Direct 2007).

# The legislative and policy context of young fathers

- We cannot afford to marginalise fathers even further, especially young fathers. Legislation and policy is in place to facilitate support (Fathers Direct 2007).

- The child's welfare is paramount. This could include a young father at risk of harm and then the welfare of both the father and the child is considered (HM Government 2006).

- Joint working is essential across and within agencies (HM Government 2006).

- Professionals must work together and share information as relevant (HM Government 2006).

- It is essential that children and young fathers both have the opportunity to achieve the five Every Child Matters outcomes (DfES 2003).

- Those working with children and families must work within the framework of contemporary legislation and policy.

# Inter-professional approaches to young fathers

## References

Burghes, L., Clarke, L., & Cronin, N. (1997). *Fathers and Fatherhood in Britain.* Oxford: Family Policy Studies Centre.

Carabine, J. (2001) 'Unmarried motherhood 1830–1990: A genealogical analysis' in Wetherell, M., Taylor, S. & Yates, S.J. (eds) *Discourse as Data: A Guide for Analysis.* London: Sage Publications, pp. 367–310.

Chase, E., Knight, A. & Warwick, I. (2004). 'Rescue Remedies' in *Community Care* 20-26th May: 40-41.

Davis, G., Cretney, S., & Collins, J. (1994). *Simple Quarrels: Negotiations and Adjudication in Divorce.* Oxford: Clarendon Press. In: Lewis J *The Problem of Fathers: Policy and Behaviour in Britain.* Accessed on line at: http://www.sociology.su.se/cgs/Conference/4%20Lewis.pdf.

Department for Children, Schools and Families (2007). *Youth Matters: Green Paper.* On line at: http://www.dfes.gov.uk/publications/youth/

Department for Education and Skills (2003). *Every Child Matters.* London: The Stationery Office. (On line at www.dfes.gov.uk/everychildmatters)

Department for Education and Skills (2004). *Every Child Matters: Change for Children in Social Care.* London: The Stationery Office.

Department for Education and Skills (2005). *Youth Matters.* London: DfES.

Department for Education and Skills (2006). *The Common Assessment Framework.* London: The Stationery Office.

Department of Health (2004a). *Executive Summary The National Service Framework for Children, Young People and Maternity Services.* London: DoH. (On line at www.publications.doh.gov.uk/nsf/children)

Department of Health (2004b). *The National Service Framework for Children, Young People and Maternity Services.* London: DoH. (On line at www.publications.doh.gov.uk/nsf/children)

Fathers Direct (2007). *Case Study (Young Fathers): Providing Support for Teenage Dads.* Fathers Direct, The National Information Centre on Fatherhood. On line at: http://www.fathersdirect.com

Featherstone, B. (2004). *Family Life and Family Support.* Basingstoke: Palgrave Macmillan. In Jowitt, M. & O'Loughlin, S. (2005) *Social Work with Children and Families.* Exeter: Learning Matters.

Frost, N. (2003). 'Understanding family support theories, concepts and issues' in Frost, N., Jeffrey, L. & Lloyd, A. (eds) *The RHP Companion to Family Support.* Lyme Regis: Russell House.

Furedi, F. (2002). *Paranoid Parenting: Why Ignoring the Experts may be Best for your Child.* Chicago: Chicago Review Press.

Gaskill, M. (2006). *Systemic Parenting.* San Diego: Aventine Press.

Ghate, D. & Hazel, N. (2002). *Parenting in Poor Environments: Stress, Support and Coping.* London: Jessica Kingsley.

Glasper, E.A. & Mitchell, R.M. (2005). 'Historical perspectives of children's nursing' in Glasper, E.A. & Richardson, J. (eds) *A Textbook of Children's and Young People's Nursing.* London: Churchill Livingstone, pp. 3–17. http://eprints.soton.ac.uk/24191/

Health and Safety Executive (2007). *Young People at Work and the Law*. Accessed online at: http://213.212.77.20/youngpeople/law/index.htm

HM Government (2004) *The Children Act 2004*. London: The Stationery Office.

HM Government (2006). *Working Together to Safeguard Children: A Guide to Interagency Working to Safeguard and Promote the Welfare of Children*. London: The Stationery Office.

Horner, N. & Krawczyk, S. (2006). *Social Work in Education and Children's Services*. Exeter: Learning Matters.

Howe, D. (2005). *Child Abuse and Neglect: Attachment, Development and Intervention*. Basingstoke: Palgrave Macmillan.

Hudson, F. & Ineichen, B. (1991). *Taking it Lying Down: Sexuality and Teenage Motherhood*. Basingstoke: Macmillan Publishing.

Johns, R. (2005). *Using the Law in Social Work,* 2nd edn. Exeter: Learning Matters.

Jowitt, M. & O'Loughlin, S. (2005). *Social Work with Children and Families*. Exeter: Learning Matters.

Laming, Lord (2003). *The Victoria Climbié Inquiry Report*. London: The Stationery Office.

Lewis, J. (2002). *The Problem of Fathers: Policy and Behaviour in Britain*. Accessed on line at: http://www.sociology.su.se/cgs/Conference/4%20Lewis.pdf.

Lowden, J. (2002). 'Children's rights: a decade of dispute' in *Journal of Advanced Nursing* 37 (1): 100–106.

Maclean, M. (1994). 'The making of the Child Support Act of 1991: Policy making at the intersection of law and social policy' in *Journal of Law and Society* 21: 505–519.

Parliament (1989). *Children Act 1989*. London: HMSO.

Powell, C. & Ireland, L. (2006). 'Protecting children: the nurse's role' in Glasper, E.A. & Richardson, J. (eds) *A Textbook of Children's and Young People's Nursing*. UK: Churchill Livingstone, 3–17.

Quinton, D. (2004). *Supporting Parents: Messages from Research*. London: Jessica Kingsley.

Reder, P. & Duncan, S. (2004). 'Making the most of the Victoria Climbie Inquiry Report' in *Child Abuse Review* 13: 95–114.

Reeves, J. (2003). *They Should Still Be Out Playing: A Contemporary Analysis of Young Pregnant Women/Mothers in the Care System*. Unpublished thesis for Master of Philosophy in Social Work. University of Kent, Canterbury.

Reeves, J. (2006). *'You've got to keep your head on.' A study of the stories young male service users tell about the transition to fatherhood*. Unpublished thesis: The Open University.

Rose, P. (2007). 'Legal and ethical emergency care of children' in Cleaver, K .& Webb, J. *Emergency Care of Children and Young People*. Oxford: Blackwell Publishing.

Social Exclusion Unit (1999). *Teenage Pregnancy*. Social Exclusion Unit.

United Nations General Assembly (1989). *United Nations Convention on the Rights of the Child 1989*. Geneva: UN.

Webb, J. (2007). 'Safeguarding and protecting children' in Cleaver, K. & Webb, J. (eds) *Emergency Care of Children and Young People*. Oxford: Blackwell Publishing.

White, R., Carr, A. P. & Lowe, N. (2002). *The Children Act in Practice*. 3rd edn. London:  Butterworths Law.

# Chapter 3
# 'I've got to release it': Sexual health and young men
**Ros Delaney**

## Young men and sexual health: a recent snapshot

Unprotected sexual intercourse between teenagers has many serious public health and societal consequences, particularly the transmission of sexually transmitted infections and HIV (Murphy & Bennett 1998). Rising infection rates, the arrival of the HIV epidemic in the 1980s, evidence of increased risk taking and often poor control of infections, have all raised the level of concern among health professionals, the government and the public (Department of Health 2001b). It is well documented that Britain has the highest teenage pregnancy rate in Europe and those who continue with the pregnancy are the less advantaged in society and often require the help and assistance of the state thereafter (Teenage Pregnancy Unit 2004). The issue of teenage pregnancy has been at the forefront of social consciousness for different reasons for a long time (Carabine 2001) and this is reflected in the various government initiatives to reduce the 'problem', such as the creation of the Child Support Agency (CSA) in 1993 and the Social Exclusion Unit in 1999. The link between poverty and poor health was a focus for the new Labour government in 1997 and this resulted in many initiatives including the establishment of the Social Exclusion Unit (SEU) and the Teenage Pregnancy Unit (TPU).

The SEU and TPU have presented many reports regarding teenage pregnancy, its causes, its consequences and ways to reduce exclusion. When teenage pregnancy is discussed the focus is usually on young girls with a particular lack of information for young men. However the statement that young men 'were half the problem and half the solution' (SEU 1999) acknowledged, for the first time, the presence of young men. It recommended that special efforts were needed to bring men into touch with their responsibilities and the consequences of sex and fatherhood.

These special efforts culminated in the provision of sexual health services such as contraception and screening for young people (DH 1999). There was a proliferation of clinics provided separately for young people, which featured music and posters to entice young people to attend, and clinics were held at convenient after school hours or even in school premises to facilitate attendance for young people (DfES 2007). These initiatives were generally welcomed but the clinics are attended by a token number of young men and this is the crux of the problem. For young men to become 'half the solution' their sexual health issues need to be addressed. Philip *et al.* (2006) inform us that poor sexual health in itself may lead to further exclusion, being both diagnostic of and a causative factor in social exclusion. Therefore, the key issues for young men are:

● prevention of early initiation of sex

● promoting safer sex when sexual activity has started and

● reducing the morbidity and mortality associated with adolescent sexual and reproductive activity (WHO 2004).

Their poor sexual health and under-use of contraception may be a consequence of a cascade of events including lack of provision of service for young men, poor sexual health information, absent sexual health education (due perhaps to exclusion from school) and also sex education that fails to take note of the prevailing concepts of masculinity. Contraceptive services have traditionally catered for women and new services for young people may have been set up without staff preparing to deal with young men.

Consequently, understanding boys, their behaviour and their needs can assist service providers, health practitioners and school nurses make boys 'half the solution' in tackling teenage pregnancy and promoting better sexual health for them. This chapter is, therefore concerned with the sexual health of young men. Firstly, the chapter will consider the patterns of teenage sexuality. Secondly, a look at the development of male sexuality incorporating some thoughts on male sex drive and risk behaviour will be presented. Thirdly, the chapter will discuss some of the influences on male adolescent behaviour. Fourthly, the chapter considers sexual health for young men, focusing on contemporary issues, e.g. sexually transmitted infections, safer sex etc. Guidelines for engaging men in services will also be included. The chapter argues that greater understanding and awareness of all of these issues by health practitioners can be used to effectively promote sexual health amongst young men.

## Setting the scene: patterns of teenage sexuality

## Teenage sexuality

When considering sexual health issues for young men it is important to consider wider patterns in teenage sexual behaviour.

### Changing patterns of teenage sexual activity

An increase in the proportion of women for whom hetero-sexual intercourse occurred before the age of 16 is evident: the proportion of women under 30 when interviewed who reported intercourse before 16 is higher than for women aged 30 and over (Wellings *et al.* 2001).

Average age at first intercourse has declined from the age of 21 to 17 for young women and from 20 to 17 for young men (Wellings *et al.* 2001). Furthermore these statistics show that one in five teenagers under 16 are sexually active. Wellings (2001) tells us that this activity is not similar through all classes, with teenagers from middle class families having their first sexual experience two years later than those from a working class family.

In England in 2001 there were 38,439 conceptions to under-18-year-olds, a conception rate of 42.3 per thousand. There is also a significant association between educational levels and abortion with Wellings *et al.* (2001) also informing us that 29% of these sexually active young women who left school at 16 with no qualifications had a child at the age of 17 or younger.

Among 16–24-year-olds the occurrence of first intercourse before the age of 16 and the non-use of contraception among young boys and girls was higher amongst those who did not live with both parents at 16 and those who left school at the age of 16 (Wellings *et al.* 2001).

Trends in sexually transmitted infections amongst young people are a recent issue for concern. New diagnoses of infections between 2005 and 2006 rose by 2%. The National Chlamydia Screening Programme (NCSP) has detected a 'positivity' of 10% amongst men and women aged under 25. The risk factors for each group vary – for men infection rates are higher in the 20–24 age group (La Montagne *et al.* 2004). While much has been done to raise the profile of sexual health in recent years, Evans (2007) argues that sexual health needs a long-term approach and immediate input. In Britain we are still living with an approach dominated by a 'contraceptive mentality' where the overriding fear of pregnancy is paramount. Evans (2007) directs us to the importance of having a message of contraception and 'contra' infection (using condoms) normalised in sex education and sexual health clinics.

## Sexual development: some underpinning theoretical constructions

**Sexual development**

While the above statistics demonstrate the sexual activity of both young men and women, dominant masculine discourses suggest that young men have 'natural' sexual desires (Evans 2003) and these desires are stronger than women's. An exploration and understanding of boys' sexuality and its development will aid health professionals in developing sexual health services for them. Biological development in the area of sexual development is often focused on puberty, when the adolescent's body develops its adult shape and reproductive functioning and the hormonal changes affect sex drives in complex ways. Peate (2007) suggests that biological differences allow the classification of men and women and that behaviours explained by biology in this model, such as 'boys will be boys' (Peate 2007) remove guilt and responsibility for some behaviours by boys.

MacEachron and Bolton (1988) argue that viewed from a developmental perspective, adolescent male sexuality is the time of transition from childhood experimentation to adult sexuality. This transition is often difficult because of misinformation about sexuality, cultural expectations of masculinity defined by gender roles, and differential parental and peer socialisation of males from infancy through adolescence. The quest for adult masculinity and sexuality for adolescent males is further complicated by a social context which often exaggerates fears of femininity and homophobia. Martino (1999) comments that many boys learn to establish their masculinity in opposition to femininity. These practices involve establishing a heterosexual masculinity as the norm, making girls and femininity subordinate.

**Table 3.1**

## Some common descriptions associated with masculinity and femininity

(adapted from Peate 2007 and Chambers *et al.* 2004)

| Masculine | Feminine |
|---|---|
| competitive | non-competitive |
| non-co-operative | co-operative |
| strong | gentle |
| powerful | weak |
| self-reliant | dependent |
| unemotional | emotional |

Courtenay (2000) reinforces these arguments by suggesting that contemporary beliefs and behaviours incorporated in hetero-sexual masculinity are: a denial of weakness or vulnerability, the need for physical control, dismissal of any need for help, a ceaseless interest in sex, display of aggression and physical dominance. Chambers *et al.* (2000) also identified many of these characteristics but also state that heterosexual masculinity often uses verbal sexual harassment towards girls and suspected homosexual boys in response to perceived threats to their masculinity. This resulted in the labelling of offenders against the hetero-normative form of masculinity with names such as 'wuss' referring to a slang name for female genitals (Martino 1999). Heterosexual masculinity with its misogynistic views and bullying of 'effeminate' boys is culturally dominant, particularly amongst working class males and is a form of hegemonic masculinity (Mac an Ghaill 1996). An understanding of this type of masculinity is important to healthcare practitioners in dealing with young men's sexual health as it may explain their reluctance to attend for contraception or to ask for information regarding symptoms of a sexually transmitted infection.

**Figure 3.1**  **Features of hegemonic heterosexuality as seen by adolescent boys** (adapted from Chambers *et al.* 2004)

- The subordination of girls (and boys who fail to conform to hegemonic heterosexual masculinity) to ensure the reproduction of male power.
- Heterosexual policing of sexual morality by boys which involves 'double standards' related to a description of macho sexuality and performance for themselves and an application of a strict morality code for girls.
- Contraception as a girls' responsibility and also girls are responsible for 'how far they could go'.
- Boys often objectify girls when discussing sex.
- Boys are disruptive in sex education classes and use it as an excuse to have a laugh and treated the sessions with disdain. They are unlikely to put themselves in a subordinate position and ask for advice regarding sex and sexuality even when it is required.

### Repercussions for Health Practitioners

- Hegemonic masculinity can explain a boy's reluctance to use condoms and reject contraception as 'girl's business'.
- Proving manhood, by getting a girl pregnant leading to teenage pregnancy, may be a feature of heterosexual masculinity.
- Viewing young people in terms of traditional sex roles or a particular form of masculinity affects the way they view their developing sexuality and make choices about their sexual behaviour. For adolescent males, choices about their sexual behaviour are often attributed to their sex drive and more importantly the difference in their libido compared to teenage girls. By sex drive, we mean the motivation to engage in sexual activity (Baumeister & Tice 2001).

# Sexual health and young men

- Harrison and Dignan (1999) inform us that women often view sex as part of an intimate relationship, with tenderness and emotion, while some men can view sex as an act in itself not necessarily linked with emotional commitment.

- In a national survey, Laumann *et al*. (1994) found that over half the men think about sex every day in comparison to one in five women.

- A review of many research studies on sexual fantasy yielded a consistent pattern: men have more frequent sexual fantasies than women, as well as fantasising about more different partners and acts (Leitenberg & Henning 1995).

- Men also describe wanting more sexual partners than women. The average woman described wanting two or three sex partners, while the average male response was sixty-four. Nearly all surveys find that men report having had more partners (Baumeister & Tice 2001).

- Masturbation is another indicator with boys reporting more masturbatory activity than girls (Katchadourian 1990).

Some feminist writers reject the belief that women lack sexual desire in comparison to men. They suggest, instead, that the seeming 'deficit' in female sexuality reflects the oppression by the male-dominated culture, which causes women to be alienated from their own sexuality. In this view, society fails to teach them to masturbate or enjoy sexual pleasure, and 'punishes' women who have too many partners or who simply enjoy sex. When the female potential for multiple orgasms became scientifically established in the 1960s, feminists used this to argue that female sexuality was actually superior to male in the sense of being more powerful (Baumeister & Tice 2001). Even the most ardent supporter of biological determinism must seemingly concede that different cultures and historical eras have exerted different degrees of pressure on women to control their sexuality. Baumeister and Tice (2001) tell us that social disapproval is still attached to sexually adventurous females. Society has a strong belief that males' sex drive is largely uncontrollable. This social learning is manifested by boys when they say 'I have got to release it', i.e. their sperm. Girls may feel subordinate to this patriarchy and may be pressured to accommodate this sexual drive.

# Inter-professional approaches to young fathers

## Young men, drinking and sexual activity

**Drinking and sexual activity**

Another consequence of contemporary masculinities is risk-taking. Peate (2007) informs us that hegemonic masculinity and societal expectations often encourage young men to take physical and psychological risks, for example, drug taking, alcohol abuse and unprotected sex (Purser *et al.* 2001). Alcohol intake is a major feature of adolescence and is linked to sexual activity. DH (2001a) in a survey showed that 24% of young men aged 11–15 had drunk alcohol in the previous week. Courtenay (2000) suggests that the intake is related to demonstration of masculinity. Alcohol can make young men vulnerable and is often a factor associated with decision-making and teenage sexual activity (Peate 2007). Sexual activity among teenagers is often opportunistic, unplanned and affected by alcohol and drug-taking (Wellings *et al.* 2001).

Binge drinking, defined as the regular consumption of 10 units of alcohol in a single session (Royal College of Physicians 2001) is a feature of adolescence for some young people and can result in severe impairment of judgement (Peate 2007). Risky sexual behaviour has dangerous consequences. Unprotected sexual intercourse increases the risk of sexually transmitted infections (STIs) and unwanted pregnancies. STIs are associated with serious problems in health and some of the infections may be asymptomatic in some men (Clutterbuck 2004), in particular chlamydia.

Date rape can also be a feature of 'masculine' risk taking. Laws (2006) asserts that young men can see sexual coercion in dating or romantic situations as 'acceptable behaviour' and the criminal consequences are not always apparent to them. Sexual fantasies may include risky behaviours including suffocation fantasies (Harrison & Dignan 1999) whereby pleasure is derived from asphyxia which can lead to a semi-hallucinogenic state, coupled with orgasm. Auto-erotic asphyxiation is additionally dangerous as it is often practised in a situation where the person may be alone.

## Influences on Teenage Sexuality

**Teenage sexuality**

Influences on adolescent sexuality come from many sources, including the law, peer groups, parents and sex education; these will be briefly considered below.

> ### Good Practice Box
>
> ## Minimising Risk
>
> Health practitioners should assess safe alcohol levels with young men during history taking.
>
> Refer to GP or other agencies if alcohol abuse suspected.
>
> Discuss aspects of sexual consent with young men.
>
> Discuss sexual fantasies and give strategies for safer sex and promotion of health.

## The law

The influence of the law regarding sexual behaviour is not visible to young people, therefore they often pick it up from other sources and it may not be accurate.

- The Sexual Offences Act (2003) prohibits sexual intercourse under the age of 16. It may be said that the law reflects the overt - but not necessarily the implicit - sexual values of a society. Indeed, the degree to which laws about sexual behaviour actually affect the sexual practice of adolescents is worthy of more research. Of course, one difficulty in attempting to regulate sexuality is that these laws are often unenforced and unenforceable. It is one thing to make sexual intercourse between a 15-year-old girl and a 19-year-old boy illegal. It is another to convince the pair in question that what they are doing should cease because it is against the law (Moore & Rosenthal 1993).

- Young people under the age of 16 can consent to medical treatment if they are deemed to have sufficient maturity and judgement to enable them to fully understand what is proposed. This was clarified in England and Wales by the House of Lords in the case of Gillick vs West Norfolk and Wisbech AHA & DHSS in 1985 (Brook 2007). Although it is an offence for a man to have sex with a girl under 16 it is lawful for healthcare practitioners to provide contraception, advice and treatment, without parental consent, providing certain criteria are met. These criteria, known as the Fraser Guidelines, were devised by Lord Fraser in the House of Lords case and require the healthcare practitioner to be satisfied that:

## The Fraser Guidelines:

- The young person cannot be persuaded to inform their parents.
- The young person is likely to begin, or to continue having, sexual intercourse with or without contraceptive treatment.
- Unless the young person receives contraceptive treatment, their physical or mental health, or both are likely to suffer.
- The young person's best interests require them to receive contraceptive advice or treatment with or without parental consent.

The young person has a right to confidentiality also, whether treatment is given or not. Young people are advised of this availability of treatment and advice in schools and youth clubs in an effort to prevent unwanted pregnancies.

## Case Scenario

Callum's mother found an appointment card for a young people's advice centre in his trouser pocket. She was very angry as she was unaware that Callum was attending such a centre. She immediately called the number and demanded to know had her son attended and if so what for? She became angrier to be told that she could not be given any information regarding her son. 'But he is only 14' she argued, 'I have the right to know what my son gets up to!'

Callum has the right to confidentiality and the right to treatment under the age of 16 without parental consent. His 'rights' were instituted when the DHSS issued guidelines to doctors (and health practitioners in clinics) that they could consult with young people under 16 regarding contraception. Mrs Gillick took action against her Health Authority when they refused to assure her that as a parent she would be informed if one of her daughters attended for contraception. Initially the decision was in favour of Mrs Gillick. The DHSS (now the Department of Health) appealed to the House of Lords who ruled 'the law did not recognise any rule of parental authority until a fixed age'. Parental rights were recognised by the law only as long as they were needed for the protection of the child and such rights yielded to the child's rights to make his own decisions when he reached a sufficient understanding and intelligence to be capable of 'making up his own mind' (Laws 2006). Lord Fraser in his speech following the case issued guidelines for doctors to use to judge competence in young people and these have come to be known as the Fraser guidelines or 'Gillick competence' (Thistle & Ray 2002).

---

## Good Practice Box

### The role of the health care practitioner

- The majority of young people engaged in sexual activity are in consenting relationships. There may be an occasion where the nurse/doctor has concerns regarding the maturity of the young person and they are encouraged to seek specialist advice.
  The practitioner can seek advice from the Lead Person for child protection in their area.

- Confidentiality is guaranteed to the young person. There are three occasions when confidentiality may be breached (NMC 2006):
  1. When it can be justified in the public interest (usually to protect the client from risk or harm)
  2. When required by court or law
  3. When there is an issue of child protection.

- It is important that all staff (clerical, social, medical and nursing) are aware of the confidentiality 'promised to young people'. Training should be provided for all staff.

---

The Sexual Offences Act (2003) gave cause for concern amongst many professionals (Evans 2004b). New laws on 'grooming' and the law regarding under 16s caused some consternation for health carers. This disquiet was refuted by the Department of Health (2004) who responded 'The Sexual Offences Act 2003 does not affect the ability of health professionals and others working with young people to provide confidential advice or treatment on contraception, sexual and reproductive health to young people under 16.'

The Act states that, a person is not guilty of aiding, abetting or counselling a sexual offence against a child where they are acting for the purpose of:

● protecting a child from pregnancy or sexually transmitted infection,

● protecting the physical safety of a child,

● promoting a child's emotional well-being by the giving of advice.

In all cases, the person must not be causing or encouraging the commission of an offence or a child's participation in it. Nor must the person be acting for the purpose of obtaining sexual gratification. It also reiterated that advice to young people under 16 and under 13 can continue. (Sexual activity under the age of 13 is considered an absolute offence. This is covered in section 5 of the Sexual Offences Act. However teenagers of all ages will have sex and some 12–13-year-olds may require advice. This can be given once assurances can be given that these teenagers are not at risk of abuse, etc. These teenagers would be counselled about delay, but many practitioners would have been at risk of breaking the law in discussing such matters with these teenagers without the guidance from the DH.)

## Peer influences

Peers provide information regarding sex which may aid decision making about sexual behaviour. It seems that friends take an active role in each other's sex education, but the role of these non-sexual partners is largely confined to talk (De Freitas 2002). While it is certainly important for the young person who is establishing values and rehearsing for adult sexuality to have the sympathetic ear and counsel of friends, the sex education provided from this source is limited and often not supplemented by other sources. De Freitas (2002) tells us that there is a divide between what works for boys and for girls: girls confide in their friends whilst boys tend to compete with theirs. Taken on its own, this advice can be a case of 'the blind leading the blind', with incomplete and wrong information being disseminated, with vital elements like the establishment of non-risky sexual behaviours neglected (Moore & Rosenthal 1993).

---

**Common myths about sex shared amongst young people** (Evans 2004b)

'You can't get pregnant the first time you have sex'

'A boy can't get you pregnant if he withdraws before he comes'

'HIV is only for gay men and foreigners'

'You cannot get pregnant if you have sex standing up'

'You cannot get a sexually transmitted infection if you are on the pill'

---

## The role of parents

Moore and Rosenthal (1993) in their discussion of parents tell us that adult behaviour has greater influence on young people than parental talk. Anecdotal evidence to the author in a sexual health setting testifies to this; boys are often told by their father to 'keep it in your trousers' while their father is seen as a hypocrite because he has fathered other children outside the home. O'Donnell et al. (2007) suggest that parents can have a positive influence in delaying sexual activity among young people. Stanton et al. (2000) argue that this is especially important during late childhood and early adolescence as they influence their choices regarding sexual behaviour.

- Communication about sexually risky behaviours by parents has been demonstrated as a protecting factor (McNeely et al. 2002).

- Parents who set clear expectations about dating and the importance of delaying sex and who relate these to family values are more likely to have children who delay having sex (O'Donnell et al. 2007). However, not all parents feel they can communicate with their children about these topics (O'Donnell et al. 2007) and programmes of education for parents to communicate regarding sexual health matters are available, e.g. Speakeasy run by the Family Planning Association (FPA 2007).

## Religious influences

Religion has been found to be related to premarital sexual behaviour; religious persons regardless of denomination are less likely to be sexually active. Sexual values encouraging conservatism and restraint are promulgated by most religions. Thus, adolescents who are devout in their religious beliefs are among those least likely to experience early sexual initiation or multiple partnering. Rostosky *et al.* (2004) indicate that 'religiosity' delays the sexual debut of young women whilst findings are mixed for young men. Although only half of the studies examined the effects of race and ethnicity, results of these studies reported similar effects for white and black adolescents.

## Sex education in the schools

Wight *et al.* (2002) found that teacher-delivered sex education does not provide young people with the knowledge and skills deemed necessary to negotiate sexual relationships. This is also supported by a study by Di Censo (2002).

Although the guidelines on sex and relationship education (DfEE 2000) provide schools with a structure under which teachers and governors can plan and deliver a sex and relationships programme, the subject matter remains non-statutory and parents have retained their right to withdraw their child from any non-statutory elements of sex education (Hilton 2001). This leaves teachers in an uncertain position regarding the content of compulsory and non-compulsory elements of SRE. This in turn has an impact on the quality of the education being delivered (Johnson 1998, Kingston 1998).

Sex education is a subject of indifference to many staff as it remains a non-assessed component of the curriculum (Hilton 2001). Not only are teaching methods proving to be a problem, the legal challenges schools face are influential too, with the tenuous relationship observed between government legislation and schools' sexual health education provision (Westwood & Mullan 2007). Consequently teachers are sometimes unsure of what they can and cannot teach for fear of complaint or litigation (Hilton 2001).

Current UK government policy to tackle the high rates of teenage conceptions and sexually transmitted infections among young people (Public Health Laboratory Service [PHLS] 2001, UNICEF 2001) advocates a multi-agency approach to adolescent sexual health (SEU 1999, DH 2001). This is in light of substantial evidence to suggest that teacher-led sexual health programmes are not effective (Wight *et al.* 2002) and that teachers may not be the most appropriate profession to deliver sexual health information (Graham *et al.* 2002), particularly those who do not specialise in PSHE (Revell 2000). However, it would seem that despite various attempts to provide a multi-agency approach to SRE (Mellanby *et al.* 2001) many teachers are still being expected to teach the subject in isolation. De Freitas (2002) also informs us that many young people are unhappy with sex education provision in schools and often seek advice from youth centres.

---

## Components of an effective sex and relationship education programme

- Programme delivered by a competent well trained teacher
- Empowers pupils by exploring attitudes, increasing knowledge and understanding and develops skills
- Awareness of confidentiality issues, good referral links with local services and meets local needs
- Offers a positive, open view of sex and sexuality including diversity and gender and supports sexual self-acceptance
- Works within clear theoretical frameworks
- Ensures the entitlement of all children to sex and relationships education which will equip them with life skills
- Undertakes specific work to meet needs of vulnerable and marginalised children and young people
- Provided early (before puberty) and continues throughout the school years
- Reinforces messages, such as delay of intercourse for younger children and safer sex for older pupils, risk reduction with accurate information about unprotected sex
- Uses learning techniques that allow young people to personalise information

- Provides information and teaching on increasing confidence, recognising power differentials and in using communication and negotiation skills to equip young people with responses when negotiating sex with partners
- Increases awareness among young people of the messages portrayed in the media.

(Adapted from HDA 2001, Kirby 2001 cited by Thistle & Ray 2002, WHO 2004)

**Good Practice Box**

**Thinking through issues**

**Answer 'True' or 'False' to these questions**

**Can a school nurse offer young people sexual health advice in the school?**

True: School nurses can give individual students advice regarding methods of contraception provided they are trained and competent to do so. They must also follow Fraser guidelines. They can advise students where to attend for services or provide services themselves if allowed to under local protocols with the school and the Health Trust.

**Can a school nurse give information to a pupil who has been withdrawn from sex and relationship education by their parents?**

True: School nurses can give information and advice to any pupils requesting it and direct them to services.

**Can a school nurse refer a pupil to a contraceptive clinic in the Health Care Trust?**

True: School nurses can and do refer pupils to such services and usually will have referral systems in place to ensure that a pupil is seen quickly.

**Can a school nurse distribute condoms in schools?**

True: The school nurse can in response to individual requests, if that system is available to her/him, but not in a classroom setting unless it is agreed by the school.

> **Can a school nurse carry out pregnancy tests for pupils under 16 and give emergency contraception without informing parents?**
>
> True, but: school nurses will work within agreed protocols. The school nurse will work within the Fraser guidelines and encourage the young person to discuss this with her parents. Confidentiality would not be breached unless it was considered the young person was at risk and if so (the child would be informed first), the child protection policy of the school would be followed.
>
> *Adapted from Thistle & Ray 2002.*

## Sexual health for young people

A sexual health service for young men can involve any or all of the following:

### Advice & counselling

- Confidential advice, provided by a nurse, health advisor, Connexions PA, youth worker.
- Counselling from a qualified Counsellor, providing opportunity to talk about issues such as bullying, relationships, pregnancy etc.

### Contraception

- Condoms and lubricant distributed through a condom card scheme or vending machines
- Condoms from nurse/doctor at a clinic
  (Some GP surgeries do provide condoms under schemes promoted by the Teenage Pregnancy Strategy.)

### STIs

- Chlamydia testing available at 'pee in the pot' event days, or through postal pack scheme, Boots self test pack
- STI testing in contraceptive & sexual health clinic (CaSH)
- Referral to GU clinic for STI testing by GP or contraception clinic.

# Inter-professional approaches to young fathers

As has been demonstrated in the preceding discussion, sexual health for young people is a complex issue with many ethical and legal consequences. Promotion of sexual health can take many forms and be provided in many arenas, however, initiatives for dealing with young men are often lacking as many services were set up for young people. As has been demonstrated so far in this chapter, young men differ greatly from young girls and have different needs. Sexuality and sexual health are core aspects of teenage development and wellbeing (Kang & Quine 2007) and some ideas on promoting this for young men are now given.

## The Teenage Pregnancy Unit

**The Teenage Pregnancy Unit**

In December 2000 the TPU issued the 'Best Practice Guidance on the Provision of Effective Contraception and Advice Services for Young People'. This guidance offered criteria for development of local services ensuring accessibility to young people. It was also the foundation for the government target of a national reduction in the number of teenage pregnancies. In order to help local services achieve the challenging target of a 50% reduction in teenage pregnancies by 2010, the TPU issued special guidance relating to the needs of young men (TPU 2000). Some of the main points made are summarised below:

- This guidance demonstrated that the solution to reducing high rates of teenage pregnancy depended on increasing the involvement of boys and young men in decisions about relationships, contraception, sexual health and pregnancy.

- The TPU gave recognition to the influence of gender on the emotional development of boys and young men: 'they often miss out on sex education in the family while school sex education has historically focussed on biological aspects of reproduction and does not explore the impact of masculinity on attitudes and behaviour' (TPU 2000).

- The Unit stated that sex and relationship education and parents often focus on protecting girls from pregnancy or other consequences of sexual activity.

- The guidance makes reference to the key sources of information that boys often use: these include their peers and this can often be unsatisfactory with inaccuracies and tending to focus on sexual conquest and 'performance'.

● Moreover, when the information is factually incorrect, those from working class backgrounds are less likely to learn that it is untrue than those from a middle class background, who may have the support of parents.

● In addition, information is less likely to include discussion on emotions or relationships. The TPU found that despite this lack of sex and relationship education, boys are expected to know about sex and often experience pressure to have sex at an early age. They are not seen as needing help or support and also seeking help is seen as a weakness (TPU 2000).

## Encouraging safer sex – getting the message across

**Encouraging safer sex**

It has often been said that it is unnecessary to teach young people about intercourse but what is essential is to teach them about safer sex and strategies that emphasise the possibilities of non-penetrative sex (Thompson & Holland 1998). The 'Just Say No' campaign has had mixed reactions. This campaign, (mainly based in the USA) religious based, is focused on the idea that young people should remain virgins until marriage. A more successful strategy in this country has been the 'Delay' campaign (Adams 2007). This campaign has been taught in many areas by school nurses to young people.

## Key messages of the Delay campaign

**The Delay campaign**

● The training pays attention to how practitioners can work sensitively and effectively with boys on the issue of saving sex until later. It is relevant for the needs of gay and lesbian young people too.

● Delay work is about supporting young people to make choices about sex that feel right for them as well as providing excellent confidential sexual health services enabling them to access condoms, contraception, emergency contraception, abortion and support for choices about sexuality. It balances the message that it is a good idea to delay sex until it is a positive decision with good, accurate information and the skills to negotiate safe sex when young people do choose to take this step. Discussions of the importance of both intimacy and pleasure are also central to this work.

● Delay training courses are designed to be extremely practical, equipping professionals to feel confident about offering tangible support to young people in making positive healthy choices for themselves. Accompanying the courses, there is a range of support resources and materials.

(Adapted from Adams 2007)

## Sexual health services and young men

**Sexual health services**

The TPU (2000) found that young men, particularly those disaffected or marginalised, feel that sexual health services are not relevant to them. Young men report that staff have little understanding of their needs and they consequently think that the services are not there for them, but rather for young women. This may be because women have traditionally provided sexual health services and for women. The TPU also reported that staff delivering the services were uncomfortable dealing with young boys and men.

Allen (1991) states that young people do not access services from traditional health clinics. These clinics tend to dwell on the medical model or pathological role of contraception and are seen as irrelevant to young men. Some of these clinics are also still termed 'family planning'. Young people do not feel their confidentiality can be guaranteed in such services. Philip *et al.* (2006) tell us that these clinics rarely offer an opportunity for young men to explore related issues or concerns they may have.

Clinics providing dedicated 'young friendly' clinics are more popular (Brook 1998) with young men. Successful services for young people offer a confidential, friendly, non-judgemental setting with a service that is relaxed and sensitive to the needs of the young person (Burtney 2000).

## Good Practice Box

### Are you ready – or not quite?

The delay or 'leave it till later' message is giving young people the skills to:

- make choices about sex that feel right for them and negotiate their decision
- say no to pressure to have sex (from peers, boy/girlfriend, media, culture)
- develop emotional awareness, self esteem and knowledge about their bodies
- form friendships, recognise good relationships and explore non-sexual ways of intimacy
- choose to stop having sex when they wish
- gain knowledge about contraception and sexual health promotion
- make choices about the services and support they require regarding sexual health.

The five tick-boxes to help young people determine for themselves whether they are really ready for a sexual relationship

☐ **You feel you could say no if you wanted to but still feel you want to do it**

☐ **You can have fun together without anything sexual involved**

☐ **You each want sex for yourself not for the other person, or to fit in with friends' or others' expectations of you**

☐ **Nobody's forcing you or coercing you**

☐ **You have discussed using contraception and condoms and agreed what happens next and whether to tell friends afterwards as well as talking about the implications of pregnancy**

You probably won't be ready for sex till you can tick *all* these boxes.

But remember even once you are ready – it still doesn't mean you have to!

Remember too that just because you've already had sex – it doesn't mean you have to again – you can take some time out.

(Adapted from the work of Jo Adams 2007)

# Inter-professional approaches to young fathers

Alternative settings for services have been in Healthy Living Centres, schools or youth clubs. Examples of this good multi-agency working are the Gravesham Network Development Project in the South East of England, a collaboration between a Primary Care Trust and a council (with lottery funding) to provide services to disadvantaged people – in this instance sexual health services. These centres exist in many areas throughout the country.

Philip *et al.* (2006) demonstrate how multi-agency working can enhance the service further for young people by collaboration to provide more focused sex and relationship education and clinical services to excluded young people.

---

**Good Practice Box**

## Engaging young men

1. Young men may not wish to attend a 'hospital' setting for contraception or sexual health. Services provided in youth clubs/Connexions centres may be accessed more readily.

2. Young men, when they do attend may attend in a group.

3. Consequently they may be loud, aggressive, and disruptive and exhibit 'laddish' behaviour to cover their embarrassment – staff need to be trained to deal with this.

4. Staff should not be punitive regarding this behaviour but congratulate them for attending and looking after their sexual health.

5. Ask them about their attitude to contraception and sexual health. Use the opportunity for health promotion. Explain carefully disease processes, bearing in mind that although they may have attended sex education classes they may not have retained the information.

6. Sexual health services need to be designed with young men in mind, not as an extension of women's services.

7. Young men may be discriminatory (homophobic) toward staff when attending for services. Explain staff roles and procedures informatively.

---

## Encouraging condom use

**Encouraging condom use**

Evans (2007) tells us that we need to address the issue of free condoms with young men. Condoms are increasingly being used nationally and internationally (Peate 2007). However, unless condoms are available freely young men will not use them. At present condoms are available free from designated clinics in many areas. GP practices are joining schemes to provide free condoms but this system is not widespread yet. Some areas have introduced a 'Condom Card system' where free condoms are available at other areas such as youth clubs on production of a 'condom card'. This can improve access to young men.

Healthcare professionals can enable young men to access, choose and use effectively the condoms of their choice (see Good Practice Guide below). In some areas youth workers are accessing training to provide an equitable service in their clubs which are frequented by adolescents. Condom use has to be emphasised as 'contra-infection' to get the message of safer sex across (Evans 2007).

---

### Good Practice Box

### Positively and proactively target young men

Advertise sexual health promotion in places where young men gather – pubs, gyms, sports and recreational facilities and workplaces, service settings and the army. Devise publicity campaigns which speak directly to young men by using positive messages.

Help young men gain 'condom confidence and comfort'. Strategies for this could include:

Helping men gain skills in how to raise the issue of condom use with a partner – is it best simply to get one out and put it on at 'that condom moment', or to discuss it beforehand and agree together?

Enable them to develop an understanding of what constitutes safe and effective condom use – and have condom demonstrators available for every possible educational/awareness raising opportunity with men.

Research shows that the majority of condom failures are the result of misuse and are entirely preventable with enough preparation and support. Offer lots of opportunities for condom practice until this

---

becomes matter-of-fact, without fuss and simply routine. At this stage, a real level of 'condom comfort' can be achieved.

Talk about the myths and difficulties and the benefits and positive effects of using condoms so that the blocks and barriers – which are often imagined rather than real – can be surmounted.

Make sure it is publicised where condoms can be accessed free; it may also be worth stating the range and choice of condoms on offer.

Lack of money is also a real issue preventing many young men and boys from using condoms so it is particularly important to emphasise that FREE condoms are available from specific settings – such as GUM clinics, family planning or youth clinics, as well as some GP surgeries and walk-in centres

Young men who do not practise safer sex are at risk of acquiring sexually transmitted infections (STIs). Although a condom can prevent STIs it does not protect against all (Laws 2006). Many STIs are asymptomatic and young men may not be aware that they are infected. Information regarding the infections, symptoms and treatment needs to be given to young men. Sexual health clinics, sex education sessions, youth workers, GP surgeries and anyone involved with young people should use the opportunity to give information. Clinics offer good opportunities to engage young men and discuss their sexual health. Health practitioners should have excellent history taking skills to ascertain risk.

## Case Scenario

Gill, the outreach worker, was busy at the youth club handing out condoms to the boys and girls. She noticed that one young boy was nervously looking through the literature and leaflets. She approached him carefully and asked if he would like to speak to her about some of the information contained in the leaflets on STIs. He nodded to her and followed into her private room. She asked him had he any concerns. He blurted out to her that he thought he had warts on his penis and was very worried. She reassured him after an examination that what he had was normal, and the 'warts' were prominent sebaceous glands or

Fordyce's spots (Clutterbuck 2004). She advised him that if he had had unprotected sex or other symptoms such as a discharge he should attend a sexual health clinic for a full STI screen.

---

## Good Practice Box

### History Taking Skills

Avoid using body language or facial expressions which are judgemental.

Identify men at risk without making assumptions about social class or lifestyles.

Use questions that gather accurate and pertinent information and show interest in what is being said.

Use language that is resonant with the person being interviewed e.g. 'sleeping with someone' may mean sleep to a young person when you wish to know if they had sex.

Explain why the questions are being asked and clarify points being made.

Explain the guarantee of confidentiality.

### Common sexually transmitted infections

Chlamydia

Genital Warts

Candidiasis

Herpes Type 1 & 2

Gonorrhoea

Syphilis

Trichomoniasis

Hepatitis B

Human immunodeficiency virus (HIV)

Acquired immunodeficiency syndrome (AIDS)

> **Good Practice Box**
>
> **Good practice to detect, treat and prevent further sexually transmitted infections includes:**
>
> Physical examination
>
> Diagnosis – microbiology and serology
>
> Treatment
>
> Contact tracing/partner notification
>
> Education – health advisor
>
> Reassurance
>
> Follow up

## Conclusions and implications for practice

This chapter has discussed some disparate aspects of male sexuality, sexual health and sexual ill health in order to demonstrate the problems facing young men and service providers. There may have been a tendency to overlook men in the past when discussing teenage pregnancy but there is evidence to suggest that this is changing. However, young men require different services; ones that are set up with young girls in mind do not always succeed where young men are concerned. The chapter has argued that young men may be particularly deterred from seeking help from 'a hospital based clinic'. And whereas information regarding sexual health abounds for young girls, Barlow (1995) tells us, for example, in a study for the Brook (2005), five men's magazines made only two references to condom use whereas the five women's magazines contained ten references to sexual health including contraception, STIs and unplanned pregnancy. Thus, we should not be surprised at the statistics regarding male sexual ill health.

This chapter presented some aspects of good practice to reduce infection and pregnancy but while initiatives to increase sexual health in males are welcome, more needs to be done. Further work needs to be done regarding sex and relationship education in schools by starting at a much earlier age and thought needs to be given to excluded young people gaining access to this provision, perhaps through innovative use of technology, mobile phones and iPods.

Initiatives in the community should be increased to encourage young men to access contraception and sexual health services. These services can also offer counselling and signposting to other services if necessary. Sexual health services should be provided in schools and colleges. The peak time for teenage conception is from September to December which suggests the start of a new school year with new acquaintances is significant (DfES 2007). Safer sex and sexual health promotion is the key message. If we make discussions about safer sex the norm in schools (Evans 2007) and clinics, infections will be reduced and teenage pregnancy prevented. This message needs to be reinforced by all practitioners, parents and the media. Healthcare practitioners need to understand the behaviour of young men in setting up services and should keep updated in all aspects of male sexual health.

But while we strive for a comprehensive sexual health service for young men and all the positive consequences that this may bring, perhaps we should think less of a 'components' model and more about a holistic model. Harrison & Dignan (1999: 75) tell us that if we wish to carry forward the debate regarding men's sexual health we as health providers need to 'construct, identify and promulgate these images of a sexually healthy male'.

## Key messages from research:

- The rate of chlamydial infection in people under 25 is 10% (LaMontagne *et al.* 2004).
- Sexual activity among teenagers is often opportunistic, unplanned and affected by alcohol and drug-taking. (Wellings *et al.* 2001).
- Young men are less likely to access PCT clinics or their GP for contraception (DfES 2007).
- Young men influence their partners' choice and use of contraception, yet their knowledge levels are poor (DfES 2006).
- Women view sex as part of an intimate relationship while

men view sex as an act in itself not necessarily linked with emotional commitment (Harrison & Dignan 1999).

- Parents can have a positive influence in delaying sexual activity among young people (O'Donnell *et al.* 2007).

- Teacher-delivered sex education does not provide young people with the knowledge and skills deemed necessary to negotiate sexual relationships (Di Censo 2002, Wight *et al.* 2002).

- Multi-agency working can enhance the service for young people further by collaboration to provide more focused sex and relationship education and clinical services to excluded young people (Philip *et al.* 2006).

# References

Adams, J. (2007). 'Introduction to Delay work, R U Ready – Or Not Quite Yet? Supporting young people to delay early sex' in *National Association for Contraception Nurses and Sexual Health Journal*, March 2007.

Allen, I. (1991). *Family Planning and Pregnancy Counselling Projects for Young People.* London: Policy Studies Institute.

Baumeister, T. & Tice, D. (2001). *The Social Dimension of Sex.* Massachusetts:Allyn & Bacon.

Brook (1998). *Someone with a smile would be your best bet.* London: Brook. www.brook.org.uk

Brook (2005). *The choreography of condom use: how, not just if young people use condoms. A report for the Brook by The Centre of Sexual Health*, Southampton University.

Burtney, E.(2000). *Briefing Paper on Teenage Sexuality in Scotland.* Edinburgh: Health Education Board for Scotland.

Carabine, J. (2001). 'Unmarried motherhood 1830–1990: A genealogical analysis' in Wetherell, M., Taylor, S. & Yates, S.J. (eds) (2001) *Discourse as Data: A Guide for Analysis.* London: Sage Publications, pp. 367–310.

Chambers, D., Tincknell, E. & Van Loon, J.  (2004). 'Peer regulation of teenage sexual identities' in *Gender and Education* 16(3) Sept: 397–415.

Clutterbuck, D. (2004). *Sexually Transmitted Infections and HIV.* London: Elsevier Mosby.

Courtenay, W. (2000). 'Constructions of masculinity and their influence on men's well-being: A theory of gender and health' in *Social Science & Medicine* 50:1385–1401.

Department for Education and Employment (2000). *Sex and Relationship Guidance: Draft for Consultation* 16 March 2000. London: DfEE.

Department of Health (1999) *Social Exclusion Report on Teenage Pregnancy*, HMSO.

Department of Health (2001). *The National Strategy for Sexual Health and HIV.* London: HMSO.

Department of Health (2004). Gateway reference Number 3382 *Best Practice Guidance for Doctors and Other Health Professionals on the Provision of Advice and Treatment to Young People  under 16 on Contraception, Sexual and Reproductive Health.* London: HMSO.

DeFreitas, R. (2002). 'Sex at school' in *Positive Nation*, issue 76, available online at: http://www.positivenation.co.uk/issue76/ContentsPage76.htm

DfES (2007). *Improving Access to Sexual Health Services for Young People in Further Education Settings, Every Child Matters: Change for Children.* London: HMSO.

Di Censo,  A. (2002). 'Interventions to reduce unintended pregnancies among adolescents: Systematic review of randomised controlled trial' in *British Medical Journal* 324(7351): 1426–1430.

Evans, D.T. (2004a). 'The trouble with men is…Highlighting sexual health' in *Nursing in Practice* July/Aug: 36.

Evans, D.T. (2004b). *Sexual Health Skills; Distance Learning Programme.* London: Royal College of Nursing.

Evans, D.T. (2007). 'What should be done to stem the rise in STIs?' in *Independent Nurse* 3 September 16–17, www.healthcarerepublic.com:18

Evans, M. (2003). *Love: An Unromantic Discussion.* London: Polity Press.

Family Planning Association (FPA) (2007). *Speakeasy Training.* London: FPA.

Graham, A., Moore, L., Sharp, D. & Diamond, I. (2002). 'Improving teenagers' knowledge of emergency contraception: Cluster randomised controlled trial of a teacher led intervention' in *British Medical Journal* 324:1179–1189.

Harrison, T. & Dignan, K. (eds) (1999). *Men's Health: An Introduction for Nurses & Health Professionals.* London: Churchill Livingstone.

Health Development Agency (2001). *Characteristics of Effective Interventions Designed to Reduce Teenage Pregnancy: An Update.* London: HDA.

Hilton, G. (2001). 'Sex education: The issues when working with boys' in *Sex Education* 1(1): 31–41.

Johnson, D. (1998). 'Urged to get real on relationships' in *Times Educational Supplement* 25 July

Kang, M. & Quine, S. (2007). 'Young people's concerns about sex: Unsolicited questions to a teenage radio talkback programme over three years' in *Sex Education* 7(4) November: 407–420.

Katchadourian, H. (1990). *At the Threshold: The Developing Adolescent.* Cambridge MA: Harvard University Press.

Kingston, P. (1998). 'Boys are left in the dark over sex' in *The Guardian* 25 November

Kirby, D. (2001). *Emerging Answers: Research Findings on Programs to Reduce Teen Pregnancy.* Washington: National Campaign to Prevent Teenage Pregnancy.

La Montagne, D.S., Fenton, K.A., Randall, S., Anderson, S. & Carter, P. on behalf of the National Chlamydia Screening Steering Group (2004). 'Establishing the National Chlamydia Screening Programme in England: Results from the first full year of screening' in *Sexually Transmitted Infections* 80: 335–341.

Laumann, E.O., Gagnon, J.H., Michael, R.T. & Michaels, S. (1994). *The Social Organisation of Sexual Practices in the US.* Chicago: University of Chicago Press.

Laws, T. (2006). *Men's Health.* London: Elsevier Churchill Livingstone.

Leitenberg, H. & Henning, K. (1995). 'Sexual fantasy' in *Psychological Bulletin* 117: 469–496.

Mac an Ghaill, M. (ed.) (1996). *Understanding Masculinities.* Buckingham: Open University Press.

MacEachron, A. & Bolton Jnr, F.G. (1988). 'Adolescent male sexuality: a developmental perspective' in *Journal of Adolescent Research* 3(3-4): 259–273.

Martino, W. (1999). 'Cool boys, party animals, squids, poofters: Interrogating the dynamics and politics of adolescent masculinities in school' in *British Journal of Sociology of Education* 20(2): 240–263,

# Sexual health and young men

McNeely, C., Shew, M., Beuhring, T., Sieving, M., Miller, B., & Blum, R. (2002). 'Mother's influence on timing of first sex among 14–15 year olds' in *Journal of Adolescent Health* 31(3): 256–265.

Mellanby, A.R., Newcombe, R.G., Rees, J. & Tripp, J.H. (2001). 'A comparative studyof peer-led and adult-led school sex education' in *Health Education Research* 16: 481–492.

Moore, S. & Rosenthal, D. (1993). *Sexuality in Adolescence*. London: Routledge.

Murphy, S. & Bennett, P. (1998). *Psychology & Health Promotion*. Berkshire: Open University Press.

NMC (2006). *Advice on Confidentiality*. Available online at: http://www.nmc-uk.org/aArticleSearch.aspx?SearchText = confidentiality (accessed 28/11/07).

O'Donnell, L., Wilson-Simmons, R., Dash, K., JeanBaptiste, V., Myint-U, A., Moss, J. & Stueve, A.( 2007). 'Saving sex for later: Developing a parent-child communication intervention to delay sexual initiation among young adolescents' in *Sex Education* 7(2) May: 107–125.

Peate, I. (2007). *Men's Health: The Practice Nurse's Handbook*. Chichester: Wiley.

Philip, K., Shucksmith, J., Tucker, J., Van Teijlingen, E., Immamura. M.& Penfold, S. (2006). 'Joined up working: Improving young people's sexual health and enhancing social inclusion' in *Journal of Youth Studies* 9(5) November: 615–628.

Public Health Laboratory Services (2001). *Sexual Infections Still on the Increase*. London: Health Protection Agency.

Purser, B., Orford, J. & Johnson, M. (2001). *Drinking in Second and Subsequent Generation Black and Asian Communities in the English Midlands*. London: Alcohol Concern.

Revell, P. (2000). 'The moral in the tale' in *The Guardian* 21 March p. 9.

Rostosky, S.S., Wilcox, B.L., Comer Wright, M.L. & Randall, B. (2004). 'The impact of religiosity on adolescent sexual behaviour' in *Journal of Adolescent Research* 19(6): 677–697.

Royal College of Physicians (2001). *Alcohol: Can the NHS Afford It: Recommendations for a Coherent Alcohol Strategy for Hospitals*. London: RCP.

Sexual Offences Act (2003). http://www.england-legislation.hmso.gov.uk/acts/acts2003/20030042.htm (accessed 28 Nov 2007). Home Office: HMSO.

Social Exclusion Unit (1999). *Teenage Pregnancy Strategy*. London: DfES, HMSO.

Stanton, B., Li, X., Galbraith, J., Cornick, G., Feigleman S., Kaljee, L. & Zhou, Y. (2000). 'Parental underestimates of adolescent risk behaviour: Randomised controlled trial of a parental monitoring intervention' in *Journal of Adolescent Health* 26(1): 18–26.

Teenage Pregnancy Unit (2000). *Best practice guidance on the provision of effective contraception and advice services for young people*. Available at: www.teenagepregnancyunit.gov.uk.

Teenage Pregnancy Unit/DH Nursing and Midwifery Council/Royal College of Midwives (2004). *Teenage Parents: Who Cares? A Guide to Commissioning and Delivering Services for Young Parents*. London: HMSO.

Thistle, S. & Ray, C. (2002). 'Sex and relationships education: The role of the school nurse' in *Nursing Standard* 17(1): 44–53.

Thompson, R. & Holland, S. (1998). 'Sexual relationships, negotiation and decisionmaking' in Coleman, J. & Roker, D. (eds.) *Teenage Sexuality, Health Risks and Education*. London: Routledge.

UNICEF (2001). Innocenti report card No 3, *Teenage Births in Rich Nations*. Florence: Innocenti Research Centre.

Wellings, K., Nanchahal, K., MacDowall, W., McManus, S., Erens, B., Mercer, C., Johnson, A., Copas, A., Korovessis, C., Fenton, K. & Field, J. (2001). 'Sexual lifestyles' in *The Lancet* 358 December 1: 1843–1849.

Westwood, J. & Mullan, B. (2007). 'Knowledge and attitudes of secondary school teachers regarding sexual health education in England' in *Sex Education* 7(2): 143–159.

Wight, D., Raab, G., Henderson, M., Abraham, C., Buston, K., Hart, G. & Scott, S. (2002). 'Limits of teacher delivered sex education: Interim behavioural outcomes from randomised trial' in *British Medical Journal* 324: 1–6.

World Health Organisation (2004). *Key Issues in the Implementation of Programmes for Adolescent Sexual and Reproductive Health*. www.who.int./child-adolescent-health/New_Publications/ADH/WHO_FCH_CAH_04.3.pdf (accessed 23 Nov 2007).

# Chapter 4

# A Father is Born:
**The role of the midwife in involving young fathers in the birth and early parenting of their children**

**Liz Gale**

## Introduction

For midwives, young expectant parents can be one of the most difficult groups to reach. As mentioned in the preface, teenage pregnancy is more likely to occur in those from lower socio-economic groups and these groups are more likely to continue with the pregnancy in comparison to those from more affluent backgrounds. Consequently, teenage mothers and their partners tend to commence pregnancy and parenthood with several clearly identifiable issues, including poorer health, poorer education and economic, environmental and social disadvantage (SEU 1999). They often access services later in the pregnancy and can be poor attendees at appointments (National Institute of Clinical Excellence 2003).

Midwives and health professionals can be dismissive of a partner's involvement, possibly reflecting the focus on maternal health (child health being closely linked to maternal·health, both physical and psychological) rather than on paternal influences. In addition, health professionals can view young relationships as transitory (sadly, backed by evidence, see for example Allen 2003, Corlyon & McGuire 1997, Hudson & Ineichen 1991, Tabberer *et al.* 2000) and consequently put minimal effort into supporting them at the antenatal time. However, it is argued here that the development of the bond between the father and his child has positive effects on both their lives, over and above any ongoing relationship with the child's mother. The support of the impending father by health professionals is also important in assisting the new mother in her transition to motherhood. Evidence suggests that active promotion of a father's role in the antenatal stages encourages the ongoing engagement and practical involvement of young fathers once the child is born (Fagan *et al.* 2007). This clearly has implications for all midwives and healthcare workers working with young parents.

The focus of this chapter is to consider how midwives may engage with and involve young expectant fathers throughout the antenatal period, the birth and the early adjustment to parenthood. The benefits of this involvement are recognised for all young fathers, whatever the status of the relationship with the child's mother, and this is summarised in the table on page 131.

## The Thin Blue Line –
## discovering impending fatherhood

**Impending fatherhood**

'When I'd done my four months I come out and she was still pregnant and, "Are you pregnant?" she goes "yeah" told me then and then she had it on the tenth of December.'
Keith, young father, aged 19.

'He came to buy the pregnancy test with me. When it showed positive he cried. He said he couldn't wait to meet her.' Nicola, young mother, aged 16.

Despite sex and relationship education (SRE) being compulsory for both boys and girls within schools, for many young men contraception is perceived as being the woman's responsibility (Tabberer *et al.* 2000), possibly because they view the potential repercussions of unprotected intercourse as being primarily the girl's problem. This refusal by some men to be included in any dialogue may be a way of appearing less culpable in any unplanned pregnancy (Jones 2002). Whilst young men may assume that girls are taking the contraceptive pill, the girls themselves find that young men may be reluctant to wear a condom (Health Education Authority 1999). This lack of meaningful dialogue about contraception between young couples, together with a sense of powerlessness or lack of self-esteem, particularly for the woman, may lead to unplanned pregnancy. For young men, unprotected sexual intercourse is a recognised risk-taking activity which they feel may enhance their sexual identity. Whatever the reason, most, although not all, pregnancies to young people are described by them as unplanned and discussion with the prospective parents often reveals that although they were not trying to conceive they were not using any contraception and viewed any possible pregnancy as 'fate' (Reeves 2003) or 'meant to be'.

### Initial reactions to the pregnancy: shock.

## Initial reactions

'When I told him I was pregnant, I went down to the chemists to get a pregnancy test . . . and then we went to his bedroom to have a chat and he was shocked, really shocked. He didn't say nothin', he just didn't make a sound.' Kelly, aged 16.

As the previous chapter has highlighted, contraceptive use amongst young people is a complex area. For women there is often a growing realisation of pregnancy, as a range of early physical signs and symptoms combined with the knowledge of unprotected intercourse start to add up. For potential fathers however, the pregnancy often comes as a shock (Pollock *et al.* 2005, Quinton *et al.* 2002) despite their obvious participation in the event. Higginbottom *et al.* (2006) report that the 'shock' can last for a considerable length of time, accompanied by the increasing realisation of life becoming 'more serious' for them. Although the young men may not be aware of it, the attitudes and decisions on continuation of a pregnancy by the young mother are often influenced by their perception of the potential father's views (Hellerstedt *et al.* 2001). Men's initial reaction to news of impending fatherhood, as for women, is likely to be a mix of emotions. There may be pride in the evidence of their fertility, coupled with anxiety over the potential changes in their life. Quinton *et al.* (2002) refer to the difficulties some young men had in perceiving themselves as fathers as they tend to be neither cognitively or emotionally prepared for the role (Guterman & Lee 2005). Pollock *et al.* (2005) refer to some of the male respondents in their study 'forgetting' for periods of time that they were going to become fathers in a way that women, because of their physical symptoms, could not.

# Inter-professional approaches to young fathers

Although within wider contemporary society early parenthood is portrayed as problematic (Social Exclusion Unit 1999, 2004), it may be the norm amongst certain cultures or groups, and some young parents may have friends or family members who are also young parents (Reeves 2003). Early parenthood is more likely in both men and women whose own parents were young when they began their families (SEU 1999).

---

**Case examples**

Keith's family is a good example of this:

Researcher: *'So tell me who lives in this house.'*

Keith: *'My mum, me dad, me brother, Kelvin, me brother, Richard, and my girlfriend, me and my baby and my other brother's girlfriend and baby.'*

As is Alison, aged 23 with two children:

*'Well she (mum) couldn't criticise as she had me when she was young. She was 16 when she had my sister.'*

---

Despite the initial shock of unplanned parenthood, most young fathers who remain in a relationship with the mother look forward to the birth and are keen to be involved in the pregnancy and active parenting (Pollock *et al.* 2005, Speak *et al.* 1997). Several studies have highlighted the motivation of parenthood as being a positive influence for young men, a focus for change in breaking previous cycles of antisocial behaviour (Reeves 2003, 2006, Laub & Sampson 2003) as discussed in Chapter 1.

Although young fathers may be keen to be involved in the pregnancy, labour and the child's life, there is often a lack of information about them within maternity records (Pollock *et al.* 2005). In some cases this may be because the mother or her family oppose his involvement, or he may not wish to be referred to because of anxieties over the Child Support Agency and the ensuing financial implications this has (Lloyd 2005). An American study found that midwives were the most significant people influencing whether paternity was acknowledged by young fathers (Levine, quoted in Fathers Direct 2002). By midwives actively discussing the importance of fatherhood with both parents, rates of 'paternity establishment' increased (Fathers Direct 2002). Within some Hospital Trusts in the UK, minimal information is gathered about prospective fathers, irrespective of the age of either parent, with the emphasis predominantly on the mother and her physical health. This reflects the midwife's role in primarily supporting the health of mother and baby through the birth process but crucially it also reflects that a child's health and wellbeing depend on the health of its mother rather than that of its father. This can undermine the father who often does attend for antenatal appointments, as he may feel superfluous to the process. It is crucial however, that midwives and other health and social care practitioners do engage meaningfully with young fathers at this stage in order to not only provide a positive role model for professional intervention, but as it is also in the long-term interests of the child to have their father involved in their life and decisions about them.

## Building relationships

**Building relationships**

The first visit with a midwife is generally seen as providing an opportunity for health promotion activities with both the mother and father to be. For many young people this may be the first opportunity they have ever had to discuss their lifestyle with a health professional. Advice on nutrition, smoking cessation and alcohol intake are relevant to both parents and, by including both parents in the discussion, they can act as support to one another. Durham (2002) referred to this as a 'golden opportunity moment' for intervention at a time when men, who may be embarking upon a new phase in their life, are more likely to be receptive to information and professional support. A particular area for advice may be relationship skills, discussing with couples how to communicate and support each other to help strengthen their relationship, but equally useful is learning the skills of negotiating with wider families, who may be needed for help when the baby is born (Fagan *et al.* 2007). Quinton *et al.* (2002) found that ongoing paternal involvement was strongly associated with the quality of the young parents' relationship, as well as his ability to negotiate with wider family members (Reeves 2006). Different midwives may utilise this opportunity to a greater or lesser extent, but these opportunities are more likely to occur during a home visit, when the midwife is present as a guest in the home, rather than seeing the couple on clinic or hospital 'territory'.

Although home visits are increasingly being reduced, on both cost effectiveness and safety grounds, young parents should be one of the groups where initial home visits are vital in establishing a good rapport with both parents and in providing a first link into clinical areas. Young fathers may feel unsure of their role, doubly marginalised by their age and their sex and will need actively involving in appointments. Previous experiences of statutory agencies can make engagement more difficult (Daniel & Taylor 2001), but if midwives can relate positively with young fathers, then they are more likely to engage with services generally (Lloyd 2005).

## What individual practitioners can do

**Individual practitioners**

Whilst certain statutory services may be distrusted, it is harder to dislike individual practitioners (Reeves 2003). The basics of building a relationship with young parents are important:

- Introducing oneself by name and asking and using the client's preferred name.
- Identifying the areas of common ground between you, recognising that you want the same thing, the best outcome for the mother and the child, are clear goals of any initial meeting.
- This process should actively include a young father and he should be actively engaged and guided in how he can help at each stage of the pregnancy and birth process.
- Conversations should focus on sharing of information between the professional and young couple rather than question and answer sessions or 'imposing' advice.
- Young parents who feel that they are approved of are more likely to respond to, and build a relationship with, a named midwife or small team of midwives rather than a succession of different staff. Evidence says that the age or gender of the midwife appears less relevant than their attitude (Price & Mitchell 2004, Lloyd 2005).

- As the midwife is often the first of a number of professionals who may be involved with the parents, their attitude often sets the expectation of young parents to other professionals who will be involved further down the line; it is much easier for young people to meet the Health Visitor for the first time if a trusted midwife has already referred to them by name and appears to have a good working relationship with them.

Although first appointments may be more appropriate with young parents at home rather than the hospital (which may appear intimidating) some non-resident young fathers may not be welcome at their partner's home and this provides further challenges for the midwife. If both parents are to be included the midwife may actively need to make other arrangements, by using a friend's home or a neutral venue. It may be better to contact young women by mobile phone rather than home telephones as parents or siblings may not initially be aware of the pregnancy. Mobile phones are also a useful way for midwives to send text reminders to young people about appointments.

It is important that services are perceived as approachable – young parents tend to access care later on in the pregnancy and attend antenatal appointments less frequently, both of which are linked to adverse outcomes for both mother and child (Lewis & Drife 2004). Reasons for late booking and non-attendance are unclear, however it seems likely to be caused by anxiety at not knowing who they will see and what will happen to them. In a recent audit of the 'Young Mums One-to-One Midwifery Programme' at Queen Charlotte's and Chelsea Hospital (Hutchinson 2007), gestation at booking was reducing over the three year period and the problem of non-attendance virtually eliminated by the use of a clear strategy of positive engagement. In the scheme young women had a named midwife and one back-up midwife whom they saw throughout the pregnancy and for most young women during the labour, birth and postnatally as well. It seems likely that if both parents are involved from the beginning then there is greater inclination for both to attend regularly, particularly if they know the midwife they will see.

---

**Good Practice Box**

**Involve and Engage**

1. Capture the 'golden moment' opportunity
2. Consider location of appointment
3. Ask after the father, refer to him by name and positively include him in first appointment
4. Plan how he can be involved
5. Encourage both parents to think about their wider support networks
6. The attitude of the professional is key
7. Use text messages to keep in contact.

---

## The Waiting Game – Pregnancy

**Pregnancy**

Researcher: 'when you found out that your girlfriend was pregnant how did you feel about that?'

Keith: 'Glad actually; I felt alright, I thought it would be a boy though.'

### Antenatal appointments

Although prospective young fathers are keen to attend antenatal appointments with their partners (over half attend some appointments and over 88% claim they wanted to, see Pollock *et al.* 2005, Quinton *et al.* 2002), their experiences of attending are often described as disheartening. Fathers reported being made to feel 'unimportant' (Speak 1997), 'excluded' (Quinton *et al.* 2002) and 'marginal' (Pollock *et al.* 2005). Sadly these feelings appear to reflect the views of their pregnant teenage partners. Price and Mitchell (2004) discuss how young parents felt their care was being based around a model of surveillance rather than support. Within the antenatal period this 'surveillance' appeared to be around physical procedures – monitoring and scans, whereas postnatally it was perceived as being 'checked up on' and monitoring how young parents were 'coping'.

McLeod and Weaver (2002) found that young women in particular relied on partners or mothers accompanying them to ask questions for them. Antenatal clinics can appear daunting places to young parents; both young mothers and fathers report feeling 'looked down' upon by staff and other clients because of their age (Price & Mitchell 2004). This may contribute to reasons why young mothers are more likely to skip appointments. For young men it is a sign of their commitment to the pregnancy that they will come to the clinic where they may feel out of place, both as men and because of their age.

## Making fathers welcome

- Torr (2003) talks about the importance of undertaking simple strategies; making eye contact, greeting them and ensuring that there is a chair available for them to sit on.

- Alternative venues for antenatal appointments may be possible. Home visits or visits to local support groups, run either by youth workers or voluntary groups, may be an option, alternatively venues such as Sure Start, Children's Centres or Connexions may be a useful base for clinics or classes.

- It is important not to over-emphasise the supporting role of the father; they equally are having to adapt to a new role and may have anxieties of their own that they need support with.

- Young couples may have transitory lifestyles, particularly if they are care leavers (Allen 2003) and change addresses frequently during the course of the pregnancy, moving between parental homes, friends' homes, private rented or council accommodation. It is important that midwives reconfirm the address of both partners at each visit and follow up those that do not attend when expected.

Pregnancies to young mothers do have an increased risk of complications – intrauterine growth restriction, anaemia, preterm delivery and pregnancy-induced hypertension that may need additional care (Teenage Pregnancy Unit 2004). However, it seems possible that these risks are linked less to age and more to socio-economic status (Hutchinson 2007). As we have seen in earlier chapters, pregnancy and outcomes for both mothers and babies are poorer for those from socially disadvantaged groups (SEU 1999). Women from the general population living in families where both partners were unemployed are 20 times more likely to die in the childbearing period than those from more advantaged groups (Lewis & Drife 2004). This report also highlights that women who fail to attend for antenatal appointments are also at greater risk. However, although the presence of the young prospective father is to be encouraged, efforts should be made for all pregnant women to be seen alone at least once so that routine questioning for domestic abuse can occur (Harner 2004).

## Antenatal classes

'Well I had one (an antenatal appointment) in Gravesend and they chucked me and my best mate out, because there was like 30-year-old mums and middle aged couples and they saw a real young teenager and they could not cope with it.' Anna, aged 17 (in Reeves 2003)

Few young parents access traditional antenatal parenting classes because of a feeling that they have little in common with other, often older, parents (Price & Mitchell 2004). Traditional midwife or Health Visitor led antenatal classes are often held in the afternoon when some young mothers may be at school and partners may be working. They may have overtones of 'teaching', which some young people may find patronising or reminiscent of an education system they recently left. Despite its name, 'parentcraft' classes have developed a focus on labour, with minimal input on managing once at home with a new baby. The National Childbirth Trust is the main provider of non-NHS classes with a more rounded long-term view of parenting but, despite the organisation's attempt to include a wider audience, is perceived as being for older, middle class parents.

Tabberer et al. (2000) remark that, contrary to preconceived ideas about groups of young women becoming pregnant, pregnancy may actually remove and isolate them from their peers. This may well be a similar experience for young fathers. Within Price and Mitchell's (2004) study, peer orientated antenatal education was the primary expressed need.

## Targeting teenagers

- Classes specifically for young parents tend to be better attended by the target group (Higginbottom *et al.* 2006, Hutchinson 2007) than traditional classes, with some being run along multidisciplinary lines, including advice on budgeting, housing and returning to education and employment.

- With smaller numbers than some traditional classes, information can be discussed rather than taught and allows young people to ask the questions they want answering. An important aspect of this is that other young people in the group can offer their own views, thus empowering them.

- This can work well as a rolling programme with parents at different stages of pregnancy as well as recently delivered young parents coming back to the group to share their experiences. For many young people building confidence and self-esteem is particularly important in empowering them to decide how they want their labour to be and how to be effective parents.

- Finding suitable venues can be difficult as young people are primarily reliant on public transport, so a central location is important within an area that is perceived as 'safe'. Venues belonging to statutory services, particularly social services can carry connotations of surveillance and facilities need to be comfortable with provision for refreshments.

- The inclusion of young fathers within these groups can be difficult for couples who have split or whose partner may not be present. However if the professional leading the group can engender a collegiate approach of mums to be, partners and 'support persons' then an inclusive supportive group can form. The 'One-to-One' scheme at Queen Charlotte's Hospital had approximately one-third of partners attending, yet midwife, Mia Davies still felt that young dads were unable to ask questions. In response to this perceived need she set up the website www.youngdads.co.uk

In some areas male workers are employed to help young resident and non-resident fathers. A recent document produced by the Trust for Adolescence (Sherriff 2007) reviewed projects to identify areas of good practice. However these groups tend to be part of a project for which long-term funding may not be available and remain isolated pockets of good practice and far from universal. The young men in Speak's study (1997) found virtually no professional support and commented that youth and community workers were more supportive than statutory agencies, although that was in their attitude rather than services.

## Making the most of the antenatal period

Antenatal education could equally be undertaken within the young person's own home on a one-to-one basis and this may make it easier for the father to be present. The use of leaflets and handouts should be carefully considered; too many can feel like overloading and will not be read. In addition, levels of literacy may not be high, particularly in areas of disadvantage and amongst those who dropped out of school early (also remember that non-English speakers may not be literate in their own language). Individual sessions for young parents may be helpful; however one of the main advantages of parentcraft or antenatal education is the formation of social support groups, particularly for those who perceive a stigma attached to their situation. The formation of a social group allows young people to support each other in their new roles particularly if the group can continue into the postnatal period. Mother-infant interactions, language development in the child, maternal self-confidence and parental attitudes and knowledge have all been demonstrated to improve following parenting programmes for young parents (Coren & Barlow 2004). Although the results focused primarily on young mothers, the authors recommend that similar research needs to be undertaken for young fathers. It can be difficult to encourage parents to attend for 'parenting classes' as they are often perceived as being 'remedial' by both the parents themselves and society in general. Young people in particular can feel that they're being singled out and labelled as potentially poor parents; however if a group can develop from antenatal classes, to which all expectant parents may attend, then it becomes more acceptable. Parenting advice is best delivered informally and by example. A mixture of more 'fun' sessions – trips out with the babies, pamper sessions, baby massage together with advice on benefits, housing and child health help build confidence in the parenting role. The involvement of other young parents with a slightly older child can also be beneficial, using peer support to help promote appropriate parenting behaviour in the newer parents and to increase the self esteem of the 'experienced' parent. A similar programme for fathers-to-be is successful in America. Called 'Hit the Ground Crawling' (Fathers Direct 2007) it brings new, first time fathers, their babies and a facilitator together with first time expectant fathers to discuss the changes that fatherhood brings. It demonstrates how fathers can care for their babies without the mothers present, allows prospective fathers to hold a small baby (perhaps for the first time) and also allows free discussion between the new and soon to be fathers. The period of time just prior to the birth or immediately following it is a time when new fathers can be particularly motivated to attend sessions where both practical and psychological support can be offered.

---

**Good Practice Box**

## Begin to build relationships with parents

1. Offer support for all and surveillance only when necessary
2. Continue to encourage the positive inclusion of fathers
3. Consider the differing needs that young parents might have and set up separate antenatal provision
4. Encourage support systems and mentoring
5. Liaise with other workers
6. Tune into approaches and activities which directly appeal to young people rather than 'all' parents.

---

## Support networks

All fathers can find pregnancy a worrying or stressful time (Fathers Direct 2002). Indeed, many of them feel that their partner should be the centre of professional attention, but that can leave them hiding their own fears and frustrations. For young fathers this lack of support and involvement from professionals may come at a time when they may feel that their previous means of support is lessening, in direct contrast to the escalating expectations of responsibility. His family may expect him to 'grow up' whilst his friends may feel that he has moved on from previous shared interests (Reeves 2006). Evidence suggests that fathers are generally just as concerned about the pregnancy and forthcoming baby as their partners, but feel reluctant to discuss it with their partner in case it worries them. Duncan Fisher of Fathers Direct explains how men will usually turn to their partner if they have worries, but are left with nowhere to turn if their partner is their worry. Young men whose children are already involved with the statutory services may also feel threatened by professional help and this may not help the midwife who goes into the family for a subsequent pregnancy.

## Case Example:

### Mark, 18, explains how he feels:

'I don't know who my social worker is. I don't really, I don't get told really because I'll go mental. If a social worker comes to the house I just blank them and look at the ground or something, or get huffed up, but I don't swear or bite at them. I just look at the floor. . . If they ask me a nice question, yeah I will speak to them, if they talk about social workers and carry on talking about it, I won't talk to them. It's just, I don't know, its hard.'

An increasing recognition of maternal antenatal depression has led to studies of paternal levels of distress and depression in the transition to fatherhood. Buist *et al.* (2003) found that paternal distress was higher in the antenatal period than postnatally, with younger age, shorter length of relationship, unplanned pregnancy and part-time employment significant risk factors. These may be linked to the men's self esteem, or to the work environment, with control at work helping enable men to effect the transition to parenthood. Whilst not conclusive, this distress may affect the quality of the relationship with their child. However with maternal antenatal depression only now being recognised as significant (NICE 2007), it would seem likely that the routine screening for paternal depression is some way off.

Women traditionally look to other women for support during pregnancy, and for young women it is primarily their own mothers (Tabberer *et al.* 2000, Reeves 2003). Many reports emphasise the importance of the role of the maternal grandmother in encouraging or minimising the relationship between the young couple and the father's involvement in pregnancy and parenthood (Gavin *et al.* 2002). Young, black fathers in Pollock's report (2006) felt pushed out by grandmothers at antenatal appointments, a scenario which can continue after the birth. Maternal grandmothers may be perceived by their daughters as having knowledge based on their own experiences as mothers and they may be more influential for girls who live at home, particularly if the father is non-resident. For midwives and other health professionals it is important to find a middle ground, supporting the mother, acknowledging the experience and interest of the grandmother and empowering the father, through an inclusive approach, in his relationship with his partner and future child.

## The Big Day – labour and delivery

**Labour and delivery**

'I didn't feel alright because I wasn't in there when she gave birth her mum was'.

Researcher: 'Why was that?'

'I don't know, they wouldn't let me in, they made me sit in a little room till she had it then went in'. Keith, aged 19.

### Father's role in labour

Despite an increased incidence of complications during pregnancy, young mothers have a lower incidence of intervention during labour, including fewer caesarean or forceps deliveries (Heazell & Gibbs 2005). Within most NHS Trusts the number of birth supporters accompanying a mother in labour is restricted. Although the wishes of the woman in labour are paramount, some may find themselves having to choose between their partner, their mothers or other birth supporters. In Britain, more than 9 out of 10 fathers are at the birth of their child (McCarthy 2005). Often mothers and midwives expect the fathers to be present and although midwives may welcome fathers into the delivery room this welcome may not always be apparent for young fathers. Midwives may view the maternal grandmother as the mother's main support (Shakespear 2004), particularly if the new father is non-resident. This view may be based on the assumed transience of the father's role and the statistical likelihood of relationship breakdown for young couples (Hudson & Ineichen 1991). In some cases, either the young mother or young father may already have children by a different partner and this may be already known to the staff and consequently, they may have pre-set expectations of the labour and who is going to be involved. The father's expectation of his role is important and if possible needs to be discussed prior to labour. An American study found that whilst 93% of mothers and grandmothers expected the young father to be present at the birth, only 58% of young fathers felt the same (Bunting & McCauley 2004b).

## Working with young fathers

- The feeling of alienation that young fathers may feel in antenatal clinics is likely to be even greater within a labour ward, accompanied as it is by anxiety about his partner, his baby and how he will cope.

- Men may behave in different ways within the delivery room, some giving support and encouragement to their partners whilst others act as a witness – being present but playing little active part. Although some couples may be happy for the young father to be just a witness, this behaviour may be linked to men's confusion generally over what their role should be.

- Once the midwife has ascertained that the young mother is happy for her partner to attend, she can assist by actively encouraging him to come in to the room and involving him in care – massaging his partner's back, talking her through contractions or providing drinks of water.

- By referring to him by name, including him in discussion and demonstrating, by example, ways of helping his partner cope and feel comfortable he can contribute to the birth itself.

A Finnish study found that although young fathers present at the birth were more likely to feel uncomfortable during the birth than other fathers, they were more likely to feel that they had a 'good' experience (Vehvilainen-Julkunen & Liukkonen 1998). Midwives should be prepared to discuss their expectation of labour with the parents-to-be and encourage them to consider what support they would wish from each other. For some young people the relationship between them may be strained or already have broken down, however this does not always mean that the mother wishes the father to be excluded from the delivery room. In some circumstances this can be complicated if there is a new partner involved. The primary role of the midwife here is to embrace this complexity and support the mother in her labour as the mother will labour most effectively if she feels comfortable with those around her. Therefore, it is important to clarify her wishes of who she wants with her and their degree of involvement in the birth and the immediate postnatal period.

## Following delivery

Following the delivery, time for the new parents alone is important in establishing an early bond between the parents and the child and should take precedence over the extended family and friends coming to see the baby. This can be particularly important for non-resident young fathers. For midwives, a continuing tactful approach may be necessary in dealing with the new mother, her partner and the maternal grandmother to ensure that constructive family relationships can be encouraged and maintained. This may be particularly important following the birth when the new parents may appreciate time alone with the baby.

### Promoting good practice

- Both mothers and fathers show similar nurturing and caring behaviour once the baby is born, observing and gently stroking him (Lamb 1997). Skin-to-skin contact, where the baby is unwrapped and placed against the parent's skin before being covered again should be promoted. This approach helps to regulate a newborn's temperature and breathing following delivery and helps to prime the mother's hormonal system for breastfeeding (Anderson *et al.* 2003). In a study with preterm infants Sullivan (1999) found that the sooner fathers held their babies, the sooner they reported feelings of love for them.

- In line with current best practice all mothers should be encouraged to breastfeed because of the overwhelming health benefits it incurs (UNICEF 1994). This is a particular advantage to young mothers who may be returning to poor accommodation, where maintaining sterility of bottles can be difficult and where damp can be an issue.

- Breastfeeding reduces the incidence of gastrointestinal upset, asthma and eczema. In addition for young mothers, successful breastfeeding can be extremely empowering, watching the baby grow and thrive on its mother's milk alone. The success of breastfeeding is closely linked to support from those closest to the mother, so the involvement of the partner is vital (Sharma & Petosa 1997).

- However, not all mothers want to breastfeed and some may be feeling tired or unwell after the birth. In this instance the father can offer skin-to-skin contact with the baby instead, this gives the benefits of temperature regulation whilst also offering a unique bonding experience.

- In demonstrating babycare activities, for example, changing nappies or bathing the baby, midwives should recognise the young parents' previous experience. Both parents may have experience of caring for younger siblings (Price & Mitchell 2004, Reeves 2006) and although the healthcare worker should be available to advise on any areas of poor practice, it can empower young parents to demonstrate their skills.

- Not all young parents will have had previous experience but they should not feel singled out or feel that they're being treated differently. Early parenthood is more frequent in those that have been in Local Authority care (Corlyon & McGuire 1997, Reeves 2003) and who may not have had easy relationships with their own parents. How to handle and talk to babies can be demonstrated by example and with sensitive advice.

Explanation of a baby's senses and developing neural systems can be used to explain to parents the importance of talking to babies – the tone of voice, use of 'babytalk' and the use of brightly coloured visual stimuli as well as explaining the potential harm of rough handling or 'shaken baby' syndrome. Young fathers, in particular may be concerned at how much they can touch or show affection to their children and this can be a particular issue for parents who may have been abused. Consistent support and affirmation that they're coping well is vital for young parents who may have had limited experiences of family life. Baby massage sessions can help them to 'tune in' to their child and overcome their anxiety associated with touch.

## Case Example:

### This is a point emphasised by Andy, 21:

'Sure Start up the road have asked for ideas for men's groups. I suggested that maybe, you know, I felt like an absolute idiot playing with my daughter, when I was playing you know, making funny noises, maybe they could have group on how to deal with that and how to play with your child and not to be too rough as a man.'

## Good Practice Box

### Positive Involvement

Clarify relationships

Encourage participation in care

Recognise previous experience

Think about paternal depression

Consider how some young people may view professional relationships

## The new life – parenthood

Researcher: 'You said earlier that you had been in trouble, you committed offences and stuff like that, and having your little girl made you want to stop. Why?'
Keith: 'I don't know really because she's got to try and grow up now and I can't see myself going and doing crime where she can see me doing it and then she's going to follow me,

ain't she, in my footsteps and I don't want her doing that'
Keith, aged 19.

For most parents having a child is a turning point in their lives, regardless of age, culture or experience. Most parents want the best for their child and particularly for those that may be disadvantaged it can act as a motivation for leading a better life (Phoenix 1991, Quinton *et al.* 2002, Reeves 2006). Keith's example is typical: he wants his daughter's life to be different to his own. This will often need professional help to achieve.

Following the birth the positive, empowering experience can be countered by inflexible patterns of care and professionals who lacked empathy (Price & Mitchell 2004). On postnatal wards women are separated from their support networks – partner, mother or others and are left to care for the baby alone. This initial emphasis on the mother as main carer can affect the shared parenting approach couples may have planned. The midwives working on the postnatal ward are likely to be unknown to the young parents and a new relationship of trust needs to be built. Young parents can be reluctant to call for help for fear of being viewed as not coping (Price & Mitchell 2004) and are often keen to be transferred home as soon as possible (Brown *et al.* 2002). At home they feel that they will have greater support and be able to care for their baby without interference (Quinlivan *et al.* 2004).

## Support from health professionals

'I don't like health visitors.'
'She keeps telling me, "do this do that"'. (Bloor & MacIntosh 1990: 163)

A positive relationship with a midwife or health visitor has a significant impact on the way young parents experience childbearing and consequently on their attitude to parenthood. In Price and Mitchell's (2004) study, midwives were described as being supportive if they were friendly, encouraging, and appeared to like the young mother. Lack of continuity of care was cited as a negative impact upon a midwife's ability to build a relationship with a young mother. In that study the views of young fathers were neither sought nor asked about. Pollock *et al.* (2006) found that in booking interviews there was a severe lack of information about the father and that few health professionals knew anything about the father, even if he was resident. Health professionals had mixed reactions to the role of young fathers, with an expectation that their lives would not change significantly (Shakespear 2004). This may be linked to an expectation that their role may be transitory, the knowledge of high teenage relationship breakdown, rationing the amount of input young fathers are offered by health professionals. However this does not reflect the wishes of young fathers who want a continuing role in their children's lives even if their relationship with the child's mother breaks down (Speak *et al.*1997), a view reflected by the mothers themselves who place a high value on the father's involvement (Quinton *et al.* 2002). For health professionals the main focus of their attention is the child, with infant health being most strongly influenced by maternal physical and mental health. The role of the father or significant others is more likely to be addressed if the mother's capacity to care for the child is compromised, because of either physical or mental ill health. Within Shakespear's (2004) study the role of the maternal grandparents was mentioned in terms of support (being involved in early postnatal care and ongoing childcare for young mothers returning to education) considerably more frequently than that of the new fathers.

## The young couple's relationship following the birth

'He had difficulty with the responsibility thing, he has only really just got used to it now. I don't know about the future because we don't react well to the stress; we argue and shout at each other.' Dianna, aged 15.

'I wouldn't say I do everything, it's just, I don't know, I do him at night, all night, get up about 5 o'clock in the morning, or well she shoves me "you going to get out of bed and sort him out?" And I do housework and all.' Mark, aged 18.

The degree of romantic involvement between the young parents is the most indicative factor for involvement in childrearing (Gavin *et al.* 2002); this is also reflected in the parents' own view, although Quinton *et al.* (2002) found that both parents tended to be over-optimistic antenatally, with researchers' opinions being more predictive than the couple's own. This degree of attachment to the mother of their child was also seen as the rationale for young fathers withdrawing from previous antisocial behaviour towards a model of responsibility (Reeves 2006). Whilst it has been recognised that postnatal depression is more common amongst younger mothers compared to older mothers, evidence now suggests that it is also more common amongst younger fathers in comparison to older fathers (Quinlivan & Condon 2005) and this is explored further in Chapter 6. However this is not reflected in additional support services and much of it goes unrecognised and untreated. Interestingly, the study found that those young fathers who no longer had their own fathers alive were at particularly high risk of depression.

## The role of the midwife in including young fathers

For midwives and health professionals visiting the couple it is important to include the father in discussions – whether resident or not. If present during visits, asking him about the baby and how he is feeling or, if he is not there at the time, asking after him is a positive practice step. It is again helpful if the midwife knows the couple and can refer to him by name. For young parents who may have had limited contact with small children, the opportunity to involve the father in childcare may be welcomed. Some young men can be anxious about touching the baby and appropriate 'play'. Demonstrating and suggesting how to handle and care for the baby will help, with baby massage an ideal way to overcome fear of touch.

Involving young men in discussions about contraception has been found to reduce rates of further teenage pregnancy (DoH, TPU, Royal College of Midwives 2004) and this is particularly important as currently approximately one-quarter of all teen births are subsequent babies. Initiating discussion with both partners early in the postnatal period is addressing the issue at a time when they may be particularly receptive.

Unemployment levels are high for young fathers and the rates of wages for first jobs have fallen both absolutely and relatively (Burghes *et al*. 1997). In addition because of poorer educational prospects, the type of work found by young fathers can be erratic or seasonal. This pattern of being in then out of work for periods of time affects the levels of benefits leading to irregular incomes and difficulty budgeting. However this free time enables them to

**Table 4.1**     **The Role of the Midwife in Involving Young Fathers**

|  | Living together | Together, but non-resident | Not together but involved | No contact |
|---|---|---|---|---|
| Booking visit – 'How is your relationship with the baby's dad?' | Include in all discussions when present. * | Encourage his attendance at appointments. | Discuss with the mother how much she would like him involved in her care. | Consider the circumstances, children may benefit from knowing their fathers. ** |
| Antenatal visits and parentcraft classes | Utilise opportunities for joint health promotion Preparation for birth and parenthood. | Health promotion. Preparation for birth and negotiation of parenting if remain living apart. | Involvement dependent on mother's wishes. | Encourage mother to consider other support networks – family, friends and other young mums. |
| Labour and birth | Encourage involvement with labour and early bonding with baby. | Encourage involvement and bonding. Potential mediator between father and maternal grandmother or others. | Clarify involvement – does mother want him present? Bonding. Potential mediation. | Clarify – does mother want him told or want him to see the baby? |
| Following delivery | Involve in childcare and shared parenting. | Involve in childcare. Emphasis on how to be involved when living apart. | Emphasis on importance of fathering role even if no longer together. Support for mother from others. | Has there been contact with the child – does he wish to be involved? Support for mother from others. |

* It is good practice to try to see the mother alone at least once in the pregnancy to ask about domestic abuse (although more common in teen pregnancies – more likely if the partner is much older).

** Young mothers may be put under pressure to name the father of their child in order to claim income support.

---

have more contact with their child than some fathers in employment and many are involved in some of the routine childcare.

Table 4.1 demonstrates the potential opportunities for midwives and health professionals to undertake public health and positive parenting promotion for young parents. The involvement of young fathers is highlighted in the National Service Framework for children, young people and maternity services (Department of Health, Department for Education 2004):

> 5.6 Involvement of prospective and new fathers in a child's life is extremely important for maximizing the life-long well-being and outcomes of the child (regardless of whether the father is resident or not). Pregnancy and birth are the first major opportunities to engage fathers in the appropriate care and upbringing of their children.

> 5.7 Young men who become fathers may also come from disadvantaged and vulnerable groups. A positive relationship with the young woman during pregnancy is a key predictor of the father's involvement with his child in the early years. Maternity services can support this relationship through involving and encouraging young fathers.

By asking and clarifying the domestic situation of the young mother, midwives and health professionals can tailor their advice and discussions accordingly. Areas to address may be: changes in relationships, negotiation skills, supporting each other and promoting joint parenting (even in the absence of a romantic relationship). In the absence of any knowledge about the young parents and their individual circumstances, health professionals are, at best, offering vague, non-specific support and, at worst, resorting to stereotype.

## Conclusions

Whilst the pressures of workload upon midwives and other health and social care professionals are acknowledged, the benefits of actively involving young fathers in antenatal and postpartum care cannot be underestimated. Young fathers, like most fathers, are immensely proud of having a child and see it as a milestone in their lives (one that goes beyond just an expression of their masculinity), regardless of any planning or otherwise of the pregnancy (Health Education Authority 1999).

# A father is born

The period of time approaching delivery and shortly afterwards can be seen as a 'window of opportunity' when young fathers are motivated, not only to be involved in caring for their new family, but also in addressing significant relationships, reconsidering education or employment opportunities and addressing previous potentially risky behaviours. In many instances involving fathers does not entail any additional activity, just a positive recognition and inclusion of him in discussions, particularly in planning and considering their future roles and responsibilities, and in giving thought to planning for the specific needs of young people. For young mothers to feel actively supported by their partners (or even ex-partners) with the care of the child will effect their self-esteem and a risk factor for postnatal depression may be reduced. For the children themselves, the benefits of a relationship with their father, whether resident or not, help them in the development of their own self-esteem and in establishing a concept of themselves as individuals. Midwives and health professionals hold a trusted and respected position; it is important that we use that privileged position to promote positive family health, both physical and psychological, that can have both short- and long-term effects.

## The role of the midwife: key messages from research

- Young women's attitudes to the pregnancy are influenced by their perceptions of the father's view (Hellerstedt *et al.* 2001).
- Young fathers are keen to be involved in the pregnancy (Quinton *et al.* 2002, Speak *et al.* 1997).
- Young men feel marginalised by health professionals (Pollock *et al.* 2006, Quinton *et al.* 2002).
- The quality of the relationship between the young parents is significant for ongoing paternal involvement (Quinton *et al.* 2002).
- The role and attitude of the maternal grandmother is important in either encouraging or discouraging involvement by the young father (Gavin *et al.* 2002, Reeves 2006).
- The attitude of the paternal grandmother influences the young father's acceptance of his paternal role (Bunting & McAuley 2004, Fagan *et al.* 2007).

# Inter-professional approaches to young fathers

- There is a pattern of decreasing paternal involvement for non-resident fathers (Bunting & McAuley 2004b).
- Support from young fathers has positive influences for young mothers (Bunting & McAuley 2004a).
- Involvement by fathers has positive influences for children (Lewis 2000).
- Examples of good practice exist, although remain dependent on funding (Sherriff 2007).

# References

Allen, M. (2003). *Into the Mainstream – Care Leavers Entering Work, Education and Training*. York: Joseph Rowntree Foundation.

Anderson, G., Moore, E., Hepworth, J. & Bergman, N. (2003). 'Early skin-to-skin contact for mothers and their healthy newborn infants' (Cochrane review) in *The Cochrane Library*, Issue 2, Chichester: John Wiley & Sons.

Bloor, M. & MacIntosh, J. (1990). 'Survaillance and concealment: a comparison of client resistance in therapeutic communities and health visiting' in Cunningham-Burley, S. and McKeganey, N.P. (Eds.) *Readings in Medical Sociology*. London: Routledge.

Brown, S., Small, R., Faber, B., Drastev, A. & Davis, P. (2002). 'Early postnatal discharge from hospital for healthy mothers and term infants' (Cochrane review) in *The Cochrane Database of Systematic Reviews*, Issue 3, Chichester: John Wiley & Sons.

Buist, A., Morse, C. & Durkin, S. (2003). 'Men's adjustment to fatherhood: Implications for obstetric health care' in *Journal of Obstetric, Gynaecological and Neonatal Nursing* 32(2).

Bunting, L. & McCauley, C. (2004a). 'Teenage pregnancy and motherhood: the contribution of support' in *Child and Family Social Work* 9(3): 213–216.

Bunting, L. & McAuley, C. (2004b). 'Teenage pregnancy and parenthood: the role of fathers' in *Child and Family Social Work* 9(3): 295–303.

Burghes, L., Clarke, L. & Cronin, N. (1997). *Fathers and Fatherhood in Britain*. Family Policy Studies Centre, Joseph Rowntree Foundation www.jrf.org.uk

Coren, E. & Barlow, J. (2004). 'Individual and group-based parenting programmes for improving psychosocial outcomes for teenage parents and their children' in *The Cochrane Library* Issue 1. Chichester: John Wiley & Sons.

Corlyon, J. & McGuire, C. (1997). *Young Parents in Public Care*. London: National Children's Bureau.

Daniel, B. & Taylor, J. (2001). *Engaging with Fathers; Practice Issues for Health and Social Care*. London: Jessica Kingsley.

Department of Health, Department for Education (2004). *National Service Framework for Children, Young People and Maternity Services*. London: Department of Health.

Department of Health, Teenage Pregnancy Unit, Royal College of Midwives (2004). *Teenage Parents: Who Cares? A Guide to Commissioning and Delivering Maternity Services for Young Parents*. London: DoH, TPU, RCM.

Durham, M. (2002). 'How to build new Dads' Briefing paper. *Fathers Direct*. Available online at: www.fathersdirect.com

Fagan, J., Bernd, E. & Whiteman, V. (2007). 'Adolescent fathers' parenting stress, social support, and involvement with infants' in *Journal of Research on Adolescence* 17(1): pp?

Fathers Direct (2002). *FatherWork Summer 2002*. www.fathersdirect.com

Fathers Direct (2007). 'Hit the Ground Crawling' Available online at: www.fathersdirect.com/index.php?id=2&cID=585

Gavin, L. E., Black, M. M., Minor, S., Abel, Y., Papas, M. & Bentley, M .(2002). 'Young, disadvantaged fathers' involvement with their infants: An ecological perspective' in *Journal of Adolescent Health* 31(3): 266–276.

Guterman, N. & Lee, Y. (2005). 'The role of fathers in risk for physical child abuse and neglect. Possible pathways and unanswered questions' in *Child Maltreatment* 10(2): 136–149.

Harner, H. M. (2004). 'Domestic violence and trauma care in teenage pregnancy: Does paternal age make a difference?' in *Journal of Obstetric, Gynecologic and Neonatal Nursing* 33(3): 312–319.

Health Education Authority (1999). *Reducing the Rate of Teenage Conceptions: Young People's Experiences of Relationships, Sex and Early Parenthood. Qualitative Research*. London: HEA.

Heazell, A. & Gibbs, E. (2005. 'Pregnant adolescents: who cares?' in *The Practising Midwife* 8(11): 12–15.

Hellerstedt, W., Fee, R., McNeely, C., Sieving, R., Shew, M. & Resnick, M. (2001). 'Pregnancy feelings among adolescents awaiting pregnancy test results' in *Public Health Reports* 116: 180–193.

Higginbottom, G.M.A., Mathers, N., Marsh, P., Kirkham, M., Owen, J.M. & Serrant-Green, L. (2006). 'Young people of minority ethnic origin in England and early parenthood: views from young parents and service providers' in *Social Science and Medicine* 63(4): 858–870.

Hudson, F. & Ineichen, B. (1991). *Taking it Lying Down: Sexuality and Teenage Motherhood*. Basingstoke: Macmillan Publishing.

Hutchinson, C. (2007). 'A young mothers' midwifery scheme' in *Midwives* 10(2): 82–84.

Jones, G. (2002). *The Youth Divide: Diverging Paths to Adulthood*. York: Joseph Rowntree Foundation.

Lamb, M. (1997). 'The development of father-infant relationships' in Lamb. M (ed.) *The Role of the Father in Child Development* (3rd edn). New York: Wiley.

Laub, J. & Sampson, R. (2003). *Shared Beginnings, Divergent Lives*. Cambridge MA: Harvard University Press.

Lewis, C. (2000). *What Good are Dads?* London: Fathers Direct. Available at www.fathersdirect.com

Lewis, G. & Drife, J. (2004). *Why Mothers Die: Confidential Enquiry into Maternal and Child Health*. London: RCOG Press.

Lloyd, T. (2005). *Working with young fathers workshop*. Royal College of Midwives Teenage Pregnancy forum website www.rcm.org.uk/professional/pages/practice.

McCarthy, R. (2005). 'Dads, births and babies' in *NewGen National Childbirth Trust magazine*. Summer 2005.

McLeod, A. & Weaver, S. (2002). 'Are expectant teenage mothers adequately informed?' in *British Journal of Midwifery* 10(3): 144–147.

National Institute of Clinical Excellence (2003). *Antenatal Care – Routine Care for the Healthy Pregnant Woman*. London: Department of Health.

National Institute for Health and Clinical Excellence (2007). *Antenatal and

*Postnatal Mental Health: Clinical Management and Service Guidance*. London: National Institute for Health and Clinical Excellence.

Phoenix, A. (1991). *Young Mothers*. Cambridge: Policy Press.

Pollock, S., Trew, R. & Jones, K. (2005). *Young, Black Fathers and Maternity Services. School of Policy Studies*, University of Bristol, available online at: www.bris.ac.uk/researchreview/2006/11377555468.html

Price, S. & Mitchell, M. (2004). 'Teenagers' experiences of the maternity services' in *Evidence Based Midwifery* 2(2): 66–70.

Quinlivan, J.A., Luehr, B. & Evans, S.F. (2004). 'Teenage mothers' predictions of their social support levels before and actual support levels after having a child' in *Journal of Pediatric and Adolescent Gynecology* 17(4): 273–278.

Quinlivan, J. & Condon, J. (2005). 'Anxiety and depression in fathers in teenage pregnancy' in *Australian and New Zealand Journal of Psychiatry* 39(10): 915–920.

Quinton, D.,, Pollock S. & Golding, J. (2002). *The Transition to Fatherhood in Young Men: Influences on Commitment*. ESRC website http://www.regard.ac.uk

Reeves, J. (2003). *They should still be out playing: A contemporary analysis of young pregnant women/mothers in the care system*. Unpublished Thesis for Master of Philosophy in Social Work. University of Kent, Canterbury.

Reeves, J. (2006). *You've got to keep your head on: A study of the stories young men who are service users tell about the transition to fatherhood*. Unpublished PhD Thesis, Open University.

Shakespear, D. (2004). 'Exploring midwives' attitude to teenage pregnancy' in *British Journal of Midwifery* 12(5): 320–327.

Sharma, M. & Petosa, R. (1997). 'Impact of expectant fathers in breast feeding decisions' in *Journal of the American Dietetic Association* 97:1311–1313.

Sherriff, N. (2007). *Supporting Young Fathers: Examples of Promising Practice*. Brighton: Trust for the Study of Adolescence (www.tsa.uk.com).

Social Exclusion Unit (1999). *Teenage Pregnancy*. London: HMSO.

Social Exclusion Unit (2004). *Impact of the Teenage Pregnancy Strategy: Programme Report*. London: HMSO.

Speak, S., Cameron, S. & Gilroy, R. (1997). *Young, Single Fathers: Participation in Fatherhood – Bridges and Barriers*. London: Family Policy Studies Centre.

Sullivan, J. (1999). 'Development of father-infant attachment in fathers of preterm infants' in *Neonatal Network* 18(7): 33–39.

Tabberer, S., Hall, C., Prendegast, S. & Webster, A. (2000). *Teenage Pregnancy and Choice*. York: Joseph Rowntree Foundation.

Teenage Pregnancy Unit, Department of Health, Royal College of Midwives (2004). *Teenage Parents: Who Cares?* London: HMSO.

Torr, J. (2003). *Is there a Father in the House? A Handbook for Health and Social Care Professionals*. Abingdon: Radcliffe Medical Press.

UNICEF *Babyfriendly Initiative* (1994). www.babyfriendly.org.uk

Vehvilainen-Julkunen, K. & Liukkonen, A. (1998). 'Father's experiences of childbirth' in *Midwifery* 14(1): 10–17.

# Chapter 5
# Safeguarding young fathers and their children
**Janet Webb**

## Introduction

The previous chapter was concerned with 'young fathers to be' and their unborn children. It highlighted the importance of the need for midwives to engage with and involve young expectant fathers throughout the antenatal period, the birth and the early adjustment to parenthood. The benefits of this involvement are recognised for all young fathers, whatever the status of the relationship with the child's mother. This is particularly relevant in terms of both them and their children achieving the Every Child Matters five outcomes, discussed in Chapter 2. The focus of the previous chapter was however, essentially pre-birth. Following birth the young father has to adapt to parenthood. This in itself can be challenging for any new parent but particularly so for the young father who is more likely to be from a disadvantaged background himself (Chase *et al.* 2005) and possibly unsupported by family networks (Reeves 2006). Furthermore, it is documented that young parents are more likely than older parents to neglect their children especially if they are aged 20 or less at the birth of their first child (Greenland 1987). It must, however, be recognised that this cannot be generalised but must be considered within the context of their social situation and the father's own past experiences. This factor alone cannot be said to predict that neglect or abuse will happen (Beckett 2007), although the more vulnerable the young father due to their own social situation, the more vulnerable their baby. Those practitioners involved in working with young fathers and their families must therefore be alert to these vulnerabilities and be able to recognise the risk factors that may lead to abuse or neglect. It is also important that they are able to act on concerns and intervene early to help improve the outcomes for the child in accordance with current policy and legislation (Department for Education and Skills, DfES, 2003, Department of Health, and Education and Skills 2004).

This chapter is, therefore, concerned with what makes a child vulnerable, what constitutes abuse and neglect (and the definitions of these concepts) as well as the indicators and warning signs of actual or potential abuse and neglect. The chapter is based on the premise that child protection is 'everybody's responsibility' and that it is part of the bigger concept of 'safeguarding the welfare and well-being of children and young people'. Roles and responsibilities are then discussed.

## Safeguarding

**Safeguarding**

As Chapter 2 indicated, both young fathers themselves and their children have a right to have their welfare safeguarded and protected and their well-being supported in order that they both are provided with the opportunity to achieve the Every Child Matters outcomes (DfES 2003). Whilst Chapter 2 focused on the legislative and policy context from a broad perspective, this chapter focuses specifically on the concept of safeguarding children and young people from harm. Additionally if a young father is, in terms of the law, a child himself the principles of ensuring his safety apply to him as much as his child/ren. It is argued that children of all ages have a right to a safe and happy childhood and, therefore, if there are concerns about safety then professionals have a responsibility to ensure that interventions are put in place to protect that child from harm or further harm. Young fathers also have a right to have their welfare protected. It is important that professionals working with young fathers are able to recognise and respond to concerns about both a younger child and the young person (young father) and do so within the framework of legislation and policy (Webb 2007). Tensions might arise in terms of whose safety is being protected: that of the father, the mother, the child or both.

However, what is important is that the welfare of all children must be protected and it is this which is paramount and overrides anything else including 'therapeutic' relationships with young fathers themselves. It is important to recognise when the parenting skills of the father are compromised. Confidentiality must not be promised and actions must be taken to ensure the safety of any child where concerns are raised. Safeguarding can be seen as the side of a coin which focuses on prevention from harm. Child abuse and/or neglect is the other side of the coin when a child has actually been harmed or is at risk of harm that will impinge on their welfare. Obviously, where possible, actions should be taken to prevent the coin flipping over to the 'abuse' side.

---

**Good Practice Box**

## Safeguarding Children

The key legislation which guides practice in terms of safeguarding children and young people is the **Children Acts 1989 and 2004** of which the Act of 1989 is primary.

Within the context of protecting children and young people from harm the term 'child' or 'children' is used as this applies to children below the age of 18 years and therefore young fathers who are in this age group.

However, if there are concerns about the welfare of a young father who is over the age of 18 this must also be acted upon but within the context of Human Rights and adult services. In this context, effective communication between adult and child services is required in order to ensure the safety of their child.

---

### Safeguarding children and practice – everyone's responsibility

## Safeguarding children

It is worth noting that in recent years the task of safeguarding children has become more determined by government policies and guidelines (Corby 2006) but more importantly it now has a higher profile than in the past. Additionally, there has been a comprehensive new assessment framework focusing on needs rather than abuse with a requirement that it be used for all referrals within given time limits (DH 2000). This has been further developed and is now referred to as the Common Assessment Framework (DfES 2006a).

Such changes in policy have led to:

- a greater emphasis being placed on those working with children, young people (fathers) and their families to work in a more defined way than before

- greater emphasis now placed on the multi-agency and inter-disciplinary nature of safeguarding work. The new 'Working Together Guidelines' (HM Government, 2006), were published in April 2006, along with information about the Common Assessment Framework (DfES 2006a).

Other key developments since 2002 which have impacted specifically on practice to safeguard children notably include the inquiry into the death of Victoria Climbié (Laming 2003) which identified that this 8-year-old girl's death was a result of a system failure rather than the failure of individuals. The main recommendation was that procedures and protocols were established to ensure the closer management of front-line workers, greater accountability throughout all agencies with safeguarding responsibilities and the strengthening of interagency recording and information sharing by electronic technology. These findings have now been incorporated into the Children Act 2004 to complement the Act of 1989 (Webb 2007).

It is also worth noting that the scope of child protection work has increased and developed in recent years (Corby 2006). Concerns about the effects on children of parental drug and alcohol misuse, parental mental health and domestic violence have become more central in the last decade and remain key in relation to interfamilial abuse and the vulnerability of young families and their children. For those working with young fathers it is also important to be aware that the bullying of children may also be relevant and in recent years this has been given a higher profile within the context of protecting children. Also now included in the protection agenda and reflected in policy guidance is the commercial sexual exploitation of children (Corby 2006).

It should also be noted that abuse by other children or young people occurs within and outside of families, but it is a particularly significant risk within residential and foster-care. The nature of such care will bring children and young people together who have suffered maltreatment of one kind or another. Some will have developed abusive patterns of their own. It should be noted that the risk of young people coming into care and being exposed to other young people who are abusers is quite high (Beckett 2007). This clearly has implications for those who are working with young fathers and *they should be alert to this when the young fathers have been in care.*

---

## Good Practice Box

### Understanding the policy

Professionals and those working with young fathers under the age of 18 years **must** be familiar with the policy document *Working Together to Safeguard Children. A guide to inter-agency working to safeguard and promote the welfare of children* (HM Government 2006).

---

## Good Practice Box

### Understanding yourself

It is worth thinking about one's own values and beliefs about abuse and remembering that the perpetrators of abuse have often experienced adverse situations in childhood themselves, with the long-term effects of abuse having untoward ramifications, which can last all their lives.

**How do you feel about this?**

---

## Understanding the terminology

**The terminology**

Within the context of protecting the children from harm the contemporary terms used are 'safeguarding and promoting the welfare of children'. These terms are given to mean the process of protecting children from abuse or neglect, preventing impairment of their health and development, and ensuring they are growing up in circumstances consistent with the provision of safe and effective care that enables children to have optimum life chances and enter adulthood successfully (HM Government 2006). Thus safeguarding and promoting the welfare of children is defined in the Working Together to Safeguard Children guidance (HM Government 2006) as:

- protecting children from maltreatment
- preventing impairment of children's health or development
- ensuring that children are growing up in circumstances consistent with the provision of safe and effective care.

Child protection is a part of safeguarding and promoting welfare. It refers to the activity that is undertaken to protect specific children who are suffering, or are at risk of suffering, significant harm. Effective child protection is essential as part of wider work to safeguard and promote the welfare of children and all agencies and individuals should aim proactively to do this so that the need for action to protect children from harm is reduced (HM Government 2006).

---

**Good Practice Box**

**Understanding Safeguarding**

There are two parts to safeguarding:
- a duty to *protect* children from maltreatment
- a duty to *prevent* impairment.

Promoting welfare concerns:
- creating opportunities to enable children to have optimum life chances in adulthood
- Professional responsibility relates to undertaking that role so as to enable those children to have optimum life chances and to enter adulthood successfully.

(HM Government 2006)

---

There are approximately 12.3 million children in England and Wales, with 50 to 100 children dying each year as a result of the consequences of abuse or neglect (DfES 2003). Most abuse occurs within the family and by somebody known to the child (HM Government 2006). Notably however, of the total child population,

3 to 4 million children are considered to be 'vulnerable' (see Table 5.1) and some of these may well be young fathers and their children.

**Table 5.1**

**Facts and figures for England and Wales**

- 12.3 million children (all children)
- 3 to 4 million vulnerable children
- 300 to 400,000 children in need
- 59,700 looked after children (these children are included in the children in need figure, and not all children on the child protection register are looked after)
- 25,700 children are on the child protection register (these children are included in the children in need figure, and not all children on the child protection register are looked after)
- 50 to 100 children die per year as a result of the consequences of abuse or neglect (these children may not be on the child protection register, nor looked after, nor in need, nor vulnerable)

(DfES 2003)

**Child Abuse**

**Child abuse**

Child protection is part of safeguarding. In this context child protection is then the decisive action taken to protect children from harm (Department of Health 1991). Child abuse itself is more difficult and complex to define; it could for example be argued that the abuse of children is a misuse of power and trust by adults. It could also be described as being about what is acceptable in a given culture in a given time, thus an ever changing socially constructed phenomenon. Furthermore, myths and stereotypes exist about children, child abuse and the perpetrators of abuse, influencing personal values and beliefs, which in turn if not acknowledged can determine how a child is assessed and the effectiveness or not, of subsequent interventions (Webb 2007).

## Vulnerability

## Vulnerability

The issue of vulnerability is of particular significance for those working with young fathers. Young fathers are likely to be those children who have experienced adversity themselves (Reeves 2006).

### Case Example

**What Constitutes a Vulnerable Child or Young Person?**

Jack is 16 years old and lives in poverty. He has poor attachment experiences himself and he has long-standing established behavioural problems; he fell behind at school and was excluded from school just before his 16th birthday in year 11. He is now not in education; he should still be in year 11. He has many unresolved separations and poor social skills. He lives with a single parent and has a younger sibling who has a disability. He is the father of a two-month-old baby. He is not in a relationship with the baby's mother but wants to remain in contact with them and had his name put on the birth certificate.

The baby's mother is 15 and living with her own mother who is also single.

In the scenario above Jack is disadvantaged because he has a number of stressors:

- Not only is he vulnerable because of poor attachment experiences, he has experienced a number of unresolved separations (Webb 2007).
- He is excluded from school, thus his development and educational achievements are already at risk of suffering from interruption.
- He has experienced many negative life events, which are also likely to increase his vulnerability. There is a powerful interaction between vulnerability and adversity as it may be that the more vulnerable the child, the more they are affected by adverse experiences. Equally the greater the persistent adversities the more likely they are to render a child vulnerable (Daniel *et al*. 1999).

- His baby is also vulnerable. Whilst it depends on the social context and support, parents being aged 20 or less at the birth of their first child is an indicator associated with increased likelihood of child death through non-accidental injury (Greenland 1987).
- However, it must be remembered that these and other risk factors (see Table 5.2) are indicators only and not inevitable causes of abuse (Beckett 2007). This is, however, where early intervention on the part of professionals could influence the outcome for the child and family.

---

**Table 5.2**

## Indicators associated with increased likelihood of child abuse

### Characteristics of parent:

- Themselves abused or neglected as a child
- Aged 20 or less at the time of the birth of their first child
- Single parent/separated
- Partner not biological parent of the child
- History of abuse and/or neglect and/or deprivation (increased vulnerability)
- Socially isolated
- Frequent moves
- Poor housing
- Poverty
- Unemployed or unskilled worker
- Inadequate education
- Alcohol and/or drug misuse
- History of violent behaviour and/or suicide attempts
- Pregnant or post partum or chronic illness

### Characteristics of child:

- Previously abused or neglected
- Under five years old at the time of abuse or neglect
- Premature or low birth weight

- Birth defects
- Chronic illness/disability
- Developmental delay
- Prolonged separation from mother or main carer
- Cries frequently
- Difficult to comfort
- Difficulties in feeding/elimination
- Adopted, foster or step child

Source: Greenland (1987) in Beckett (2007)

---

Thus vulnerability can be defined as those innate characteristics of the child, or those imposed by their family circle and wider community which might threaten or challenge healthy development (Daniel *et al.* 1999). Within the context of safeguarding children and thus child protection it could be argued that there is a continuum of vulnerability. All children are vulnerable to some extent as the younger they are the more dependent they are on adults to ensure their safety. However, factors that might render a child vulnerable to abuse and neglect and/or to not weathering ordinary adversities and veering off a healthy developmental path can be separated into:

- some intrinsic characteristics in the child which might render them more vulnerable
- those vulnerabilities imposed by parents' views or expectations of the child.

Alongside these general factors, the particular age and developmental stage may render the child particularly vulnerable. If those children who are particularly vulnerable are identified early, it is likely that subsequent interventions can be focused more precisely, so as to harness any potential for resilience within the child and within his or her close environment (Daniel *et al.* 1999). This particularly applies to young fathers and their children.

In work with children (and young people), the term 'vulnerable' has been used to describe:

- characteristics of groups of children who may be more at risk from a range of social and health problems than others
- individuals for whom a number of factors have combined to

place them at risk; this includes children and young people with a disability who are particularly vulnerable to abuse or neglect (Watson 1989)

● children who have suffered or who are considered likely to suffer abuse from their carers in the future.

---

**Good Practice Box**

### Thinking about vulnerability

It should *not* be assumed that children who are socially 'vulnerable' to life risks have also been abused or are the most at risk of child abuse. However, there are some children who appear to be particularly vulnerable to different types of risk and more vulnerable to abuse.

There are different *types* of vulnerabilities that children face, thus it is important to identify whether children are at risk of abuse or at risk more generally and this needs to be remembered within the context of young fathers and their children.

*Is the young father vulnerable or does he have the support networks that will help him meet the needs of his child?*

---

There are however certain groups of children who may be more vulnerable to being harmed:

● disabled children

● children who are picked on as being different (e.g. asylum seeking/refugee children, black children)

● children who are already thought of as a problem (e.g. children in care, children in secure accommodation)

● babies under one year old – the under-ones are statistically the age band most at risk of abuse; the homicide rate for under-ones is nearly five times greater than the average; one survey found that 52 per cent of one-year-old children were hit or smacked weekly by their parents (Gordon & Harran 2001); babies under one have the highest registration rate on the child protection register.

# Inter-professional approaches to young fathers

## More than vulnerable:
## When does a vulnerable child become a child in need and/or a child in need of protection?

**More than vulnerable**

The Children Act 1989 and Working Together (HM Government 2006) defines 'Children in Need' and 'Children in Need of Protection' as children who require 'safeguarding' from harm. Abused children are 'those who are suffering or at risk of suffering, significant harm either as a result of a deliberate act, or of a failure on the part of a carer to act or to provide proper care, or both'.

**Harm** is defined as 'ill treatment (including sexual and non-sexual abuse), impairment of health (physical and mental) or impairment of development' (Children Act 1989 S.32 [2], Parliament 1989). Harm also includes the impairment of a child's health or development as a result of witnessing the ill-treatment of another person (Adoption and Children Act 2002, Parliament 2002).

It is this definition that applies in relation to recognising concerns and protecting children, and as is evident from the definitions, children may be abused or neglected by inflicting harm or by knowingly not preventing harm. It is also important to recognise that children may be abused in a family or in an institutional or community setting, usually by those known to them, only occasionally by a stranger (HM Government 2006). The need for early recognition of a child at risk of harm is therefore absolutely essential for those who come into contact with children, young people and their families.

### Significant harm

There are no absolute criteria for identifying significant harm. The severity of ill-treatment depends on:

- the degree and extent of physical harm
- the duration and frequency of abuse and neglect
- the extent of premeditation
- the degree of threat and coercion, sadism and/or unusual elements.

In each case it is important to consider ill-treatment alongside the family's strengths and supports.

## When does adversity become abuse?

Browne (2002) notes that in the 1980s three forms of child maltreatment were identified: physical, sexual and psychological or emotional abuse. Each type of maltreatment is characterised into 'active' or 'passive' forms of abuse. Active abuse involves violent acts that represent the exercise of physical force, causing injury or forcibly interfering with personal freedom. Passive abuse refers to neglect, which can only be considered violent in the metaphorical sense, as it does not involve physical force. Nevertheless, it can cause both physical and emotional injury including non-organic failure to thrive in young children (Browne 2002).

'Child abuse and neglect' are today generic terms encompassing all ill treatment of children including serious physical and sexual assaults as well as cases where the standard of care does not adequately support the child's health or development (Webb 2007).

**There are four broad categories of abuse:**

- **neglect**
- **physical abuse**
- **sexual abuse** and
- **emotional abuse**.

## Definitions of the Categories of Abuse

**Definitions**

### Neglect

Neglect involves the persistent failure to meet a child's basic physical and/or psychological needs, likely to result in the serious impairment of the child's health or development. It may involve a parent or carer failing to provide adequate food, shelter and clothing, failing to protect a child from physical harm or danger, or the failure to ensure access to appropriate medical care or treatment. It may also include neglect of, or unresponsiveness to, a child's basic emotional needs.

Severe neglect of young children is associated with major impairment of growth and intellectual development. Persistent neglect can lead to serious impairment of health and development and ensuing long-term difficulties with social functioning, relationships and educational progress. Neglect can, in extreme cases, also result in death.

### Physical Abuse

Physical abuse may involve hitting, shaking, throwing, poisoning, burning or scalding, drowning, suffocating, or otherwise causing physical harm to a child. Physical harm may also be caused when a parent or carer feigns the symptoms of, or deliberately causes ill health to a child whom they are looking after. This unusual and potentially dangerous form of abuse is now described as fabricated or induced illness in a child.

Physical injury as a result of abuse is the actual or likely injury to a child, or failure to prevent physical injury (or suffering) to a child, including deliberate poisoning, suffocation, and injury. Physical abuse can lead directly to neurological damage, physical injuries, and disability or at the extreme – death. Harm may be caused to children both by the abuse itself and by the abuse taking place in a wider family or institutional context of conflict and aggression. Physical abuse has been linked to aggressive behaviour in children, emotional and behavioural problems and educational difficulties.

### Sexual Abuse

Sexual abuse involves forcing or enticing a child or young person to take part in sexual activities, whether or not the child is aware of what is happening. The activities may involve physical contact, including penetrative (e.g. rape or buggery) or non-penetrative acts. They may include non-contact activities, such as involving children in looking at, or in the production of, pornographic material or watching sexual activities, or encouraging children to behave in sexually inappropriate ways. It is the actual or likely exploitation of a child or adolescent in sexual activities they do not truly comprehend or which they are unable to give informed consent to or that violate social taboos of family roles.

Disturbed behaviour including self-harm, inappropriate sexualised behaviour, sadness, depression and loss of self-esteem have all been linked to sexual abuse. Its adverse effects may endure into adulthood. The severity of impact on a child is believed to increase the longer the abuse continues, the more extensive the abuse and the older the child. A number of features of sexual abuse have also been linked with severity of impact, including the extent of premeditation, the degree of threat and coercion, sadism and bizarre or unusual elements. A child's ability to cope with the experience of sexual abuse, once recognised or disclosed, is strengthened by the support of a non-abusive adult carer who believes the child, helps the child understand the abuse and is able to offer help and protection.

All of the above categories are used for both interfamilial and extrafamilial abuse and neglect, perpetrated by someone inside or outside the child's home. Mixed categories are also recorded, registering more than one type of abuse and/or neglect occurring to a child.

## Emotional Abuse

Emotional abuse is the persistent emotional ill treatment of a child such as to cause severe and persistent adverse effects on the child's emotional development. It may:

- convey to children that they are worthless or unloved, inadequate, or valued only insofar as they meet the needs of another person;
- feature age or developmentally inappropriate expectations being imposed on children;
- involve causing children frequently to feel frightened or in danger – e.g. witnessing domestic violence;
- involve the exploitation or corruption of children.

Some level of emotional abuse is involved in all types of ill treatment of a child, though emotional abuse may occur alone.

There is increasing evidence of the adverse long-term consequences for children's development where they have been subject to sustained emotional abuse. Emotional abuse has an important impact on developing a child's mental health, behaviour and self-esteem. It can be especially damaging in infancy. Underlying emotional abuse may be as important, if not more so, as other forms of abuse in terms of its impact on the child. Domestic violence, mental health problems and parental substance misuse may be features in families where children are exposed to such abuse.

It is important to note that victims of child maltreatment are unlikely to be subjected to only one type of abuse (Browne 2002), for example both physical and sexual abuse are always accompanied by emotional abuse, which include verbal assault, threats of sexual or physical abuse, close confinement, e.g. locking a child in a room, withholding food and other aversive treatment (Browne &Herbert 1997). Furthermore, within each type of abuse there is a continuum of severity ranging from mild to life threatening (Webb 2007)

---

## Good Practice Box

### Being Alert

Those working with young fathers need to be aware that there are many causal factors involved in child abuse and neglect. Poverty, social isolation, family break-down and poor parent–child relationships are associated with all forms of child abuse and neglect and have been cited as risk factors for child sexual abuse.

Finkelhor and Baron (1986) suggest that a third of sexually abused children have previously been physically abused, indicating that a number of common factors are involved (Bergner et al. 1994, Browne, 2002).

It is important to be:

1. alert to the possibility of abuse and neglect;
2. able to recognise, and know how to act upon, indicators that a child's welfare or safety may be at risk;
3. familiar with these and local procedures which will be based on national policy;
4. able to access immediately contact details of the named or designated professionals from whom advice can be sought.

---

Dimond (2002) notes that providing a diagnosis of child abuse is a multi-professional responsibility. It is important that everyone involved with concerns and suspicions of abuse maintains an open and inquiring mind. Suspected concerns should be referred on to the appropriate agency for management and a coordinated assessment with any interventions documented. It is also important to remember that abuse can happen in all strata of society; those working with young fathers must remain objective and non-prejudiced, setting aside social and societal stereotypes (Webb 2007).

# Safeguarding young fathers and their children

## Roles

**Roles**

Recently the roles of professionals involved in safeguarding children, the priorities and focus of child protection policy and practice have shifted in important ways. The publication of a series of Department of Health research projects (Department of Health 1995a) provided the starting point for a re-evaluation of approaches to child protection work (Corby 2006). Additionally, the activities of social workers, healthcare workers, and other professionals involved in the field have been the focus of political and media interest following the Laming Inquiry into the death of Victoria Climbié. The Laming Inquiry provided 108 recommendations for tightening up the child protection system. It also affirmed the notion that professionals cannot carry out child protection responsibilities in isolation, because if they do, a child in danger is more at risk of slipping through the net (Wright 2002). The message is that safeguarding children and young people is 'everybody's responsibility'.

## Working together for prevention

**Working together**

Working Together (HM Government 2006) is the concept advocated for safeguarding children and young people as it cuts across the normal boundaries of single discipline working (Pearce 2003). The legislation is framed within this concept thereby providing professionals with a commonly recognised and adopted framework to work within; it is a key reference point and the most recent policy document should be available within the work setting. Preventative work is clearly important with early intervention to improve outcomes (Cleaver *et al.* 1999, Department of Health 1995b, Department of Health 2004, Dubowitz 1989, Ennals *et al.* 2003, Laming 2003, Powell 2003, Scottish Executive 2002, Thyen *et al.* 1995). Preventative activity in child protection work encompasses

- **primary prevention** (policies and activities that repress the development of risk factors for child abuse)
- **secondary** (early identification of risk factors associated with abuse and neglect or early intervention) and

- **tertiary** (therapy, rehabilitation and intergenerational work) (Powell 2003).

Clearly, this has implications for those working with young fathers, their children and their families. These children are often vulnerable due to their social context and therefore at risk. Issues that lead to vulnerabilities in the fathers themselves are picked up on in Chapter 7 in discussions around young fathers engaging in criminal activity and/or drug misuse which may impinge on parenting ability. In line with policy, early intervention and prevention are crucial to the child's outcomes (DfES 2003). It is important that practitioners are able to recognise and respond to early indicators of vulnerability as well as child abuse and neglect, whilst recognising that risk factors are contributing rather than determining factors (Belsky 1993, Browne & Stevenson 1988, Powell 2003). Practitioners should be aware that it may never be possible to fully prevent and eradicate child abuse, but better knowledge and more informed multi-agency and inter-professional/disciplinary working practices will help in its reduction (Howard 2004) and need to be aware of what they should do within the context of current debates, policy and legislation (Webb 2007).

## Recognition, risk and response

**Recognition, risk and response**

The starting point would be that, in the course of an interaction with a child and/or family, you suspect that a child is suffering from or likely to suffer from significant harm. Those working with children and their families should take action if they have reason for concern, or reason to suspect that a child is at risk of harm, or in need of protection. Practitioners should alert appropriate personnel and refer to the local safeguarding procedures for local guidance (Webb 2007).

With vulnerable young fathers in mind it is worth considering the factors that are frequently found in cases of child abuse or neglect – see Table 5.4. However, it must also be remembered that their presence is not proof that abuse has occurred but:

- must be regarded as an indicator of the possibility of significant harm;
- justifies the need for careful assessment and discussion with

designated/named/lead person, manager or in the absence of the above an experienced colleague;

- may require consultation with and/or referral to the Social Service Department.

The absence of such indicators does not mean that abuse or neglect has not occurred.

## Risk indicators

**Risk indicators**

**In an abusive relationship the child may:**

- appear frightened of the parents;
- act in a way that is inappropriate to her/his age and development (though full account needs to be taken of different patterns of development and different ethnic groups);
- have significant health concerns, e.g. chronic illness, disability and mental health concerns;
- have poor attachment/bonding with parents;
- sustain injuries that are not consistent with the story given.

**The parent or carer may:**

- persistently avoid the child health services and treatment of the child's episodic illnesses or
- frequently visit emergency departments;
- have unrealistic expectations of the child;
- frequently complain about/to the child and may fail to provide attention or praise (high criticism/low warmth environment);
- be absent;
- misuse substances;
- persistently refuse to allow access on home visits;
- be involved in domestic violence;
- have physical ill health;
- suffer mental ill health;
- not meet the child's physical, social, health or developmental needs;
- be immature/young parents;

- evidence family dysfunction;
- raise concerns about their social situation/environment.

There is also a potential risk to children when individuals, previously known or suspected to have abused children move into the household.

It must be noted that the above list is for guidance and not meant to be definitive. Not all parents experiencing adversity abuse or neglect their children. The specific signs that are potentially concerning are listed in below. However, with regard to the above scenarios they should all be considered a cause for concern until further questions are asked and answered. If concerns still remain as a result of additional indicators or warning signs and symptoms then these should be acted on.

## Signs and symptoms – recognising abuse

**Signs and symptoms**

There are specific indicators associated with the different categories of abuse and therefore the following warning signs should be noted.

### Physical Abuse

The following are often regarded as indicators of concern (Webb 2007):

- an explanation which is inconsistent with an injury;
- several different explanations provided for an injury;
- unexplained delay in seeking treatment;
- the parents or carers are uninterested or undisturbed by an accident or injury;
- repeated presentation of minor injuries or illnesses (which may represent a 'cry for help' and if ignored could have a more serious outcome or lead to a more serious injury);
- family use of different doctors and emergency departments;
- reluctance to give information or mention previous injuries.

**Bruising** Children can and do have accidental bruising, but the following must be considered as concerning unless there is evidence or an adequate explanation provided:

- any bruising to a pre-crawling or pre-walking baby with no adequate explanation;
- bruising in or around the mouth, particularly in small babies which may indicate force feeding, notably a torn frenulum without adequate explanation and a delay in seeking treatment; in accidental circumstances the parents are likely to seek immediate medical care;
- two simultaneous bruised eyes, without bruising to the forehead; this is rarely accidental although a single bruised eye can be accidental or abusive;
- repeated or multiple bruising on the head or on sites unlikely to be injured accidentally in this way; these sites include upper arms, thighs, buttocks;
- variation in colour possibly indicating injuries caused at different times;
- the outline of an object, e.g. a key, belt marks, hand prints, hair brush;
- bruising or tears around or behind the earlobe(s) indicating injury by pulling or twisting;
- bruising around the face;
- grasp marks on small children or fingertip bruising;
- unexplained bruising on the arms, buttocks or thighs may be an indicator of sexual abuse.

**Bite marks** Either human or animal bite marks can leave clear impressions of the teeth. Human bite marks are oval or crescent shaped. Those over 3 cm in diameter are more likely to have been caused by an older child or adult. A medical assessment or opinion should be sought where there is any doubt over the origin of the bite.

**Burns and Scalds** It can be difficult to distinguish between accidental and non-accidental burns and scalds and this will always require experienced medical assessment/opinion. However, any burn with a clear outline may be suspicious. These include:

- circular burns from cigarettes (but may be friction burns if along the bony protuberance of the spine);
- linear burns from hot metal rods or electrical fire elements;

- burns of uniform depth over a large area;

- scalds that have a line indicating immersion or poured liquid; for example a child getting into hot water of its own accord will struggle to get out and cause splash marks and children pouring a hot liquid over themselves will move out of the way; there will be splash marks. Bi-lateral scalds of the same size are suspicious;

- old scars indicating previous burns/scalds which did not have appropriate treatment or adequate explanation;

- scalds to the buttocks of a small child, particularly in the absence of burns to the feet are indicative of dipping into a hot liquid or bath.

**Fractures** Non-mobile children rarely sustain fractures and there are grounds for concern if:

- the history provided is vague, non-existent or inconsistent with the fracture type;

- there are associated old fractures;

- medical attention is sought after a period of delay when the fracture has caused symptoms such as swelling, pain or loss of movement;

- there is an unexplained fracture in the first year of life.

**Scars**  A large number of scars or scars of different sizes or ages, or on different parts of the body may be concerning and indicative of abuse.

## Recognising emotional abuse

**Emotional abuse**

It is argued that emotional abuse is difficult to recognise. It is not as clear-cut as the signs of physical abuse. The signs are often behavioural and the manifestations of emotional abuse might also indicate the presence of other kinds of abuse. The following should however be concerning:

- unrealistic expectations of the baby or child;

- blaming a baby or young child for apparent untoward behaviour; for example claiming that a baby has soiled its nappy on purpose in order to irritate its parents;

- making undermining comments to a baby even though the baby cannot verbally understand, such as suggesting that the baby is ugly or has a bad temper; such comments will invariably continue as the baby grows older.

**The following may also be indicators of abuse and or neglect:**

- developmental delay;
- abnormal attachment between a child and parent/carer, e.g. an anxious attachment, indiscriminate or no attachment;
- aggressive behaviour towards others;
- scape-goating within the family;
- frozen watchfulness, particularly in pre-school children – unnatural stillness in a child and anxious pre-occupation with an adult's (parent's) movement may be found alongside reluctance to play and lack of spontaneity and exploration;
- low self-esteem and lack of confidence;
- difficulty in relating to others – often seen as a loner or appearing withdrawn;
- failure to thrive – loss of weight, slowness in reaching the development milestones, lethargy, tiredness, withdrawal or very aggressive tendencies may all point to a history of ill treatment;
- excessive crying – may provoke parental abuse;
- parental attitude – parents may handle the child in an unfeeling or mechanical way, or cause unnecessary delay in seeking medical advice; on the other hand the mother may express undue anxiety.

## Recognising Sexual Abuse

**Sexual abuse**

It is important to understand that boys and girls of all ages may be sexually abused but are often afraid of saying anything due to both guilt and fear. Thus recognition can be difficult unless the child discloses and is believed.

**Some physical indicators associated with this form of abuse include:**

- pain or itching of the genital area;
- blood on underclothes;

- pregnancy in a younger girl where the identity of the father is not disclosed;
- physical symptoms such as injuries to the genital or anal area, bruising to the buttocks, abdomen and thighs, sexually transmitted disease, presence of semen on vagina, anus, external genitalia or clothing.

**Some behavioural indicators associated with this form of abuse include:**

- inappropriately sexualised conduct;
- sexually explicit behaviour, play or conversation, inappropriate to the child's age and stage of development;
- continual and inappropriate or excessive masturbation;
- self-harm – eating disorder, self mutilation and suicide attempts;
- involvement in prostitution or indiscriminate choice of sexual partners;
- an anxious unwillingness to remove clothes, e.g. at sports events or medical examination, although this may also be related to cultural norms or physical difficulties.

## Recognising neglect

**Recognising neglect**

**Evidence of neglect is built up over a period of time and can cover different aspects of parenting. Indicators and concerns include:**

- failure of the parents to meet the basic essential needs, e.g. hygiene, feeding, clothes, warmth or medical care;
- a child who is listless, apathetic and unresponsive with no apparent medical cause;
- failure to grow and develop within normal, expected pattern, possibly with accompanying weight loss;
- the child thrives away from the home environment;
- child frequently absent from school;
- child left with adults who are intoxicated or violent;
- child abandoned or left alone for excessive periods.

## The unborn child

## The unborn child

In some circumstances workers and professionals within the different agencies are able to anticipate the likelihood of significant harm with regard to an expected baby. If the young parents are attending antenatal care, professionals should be alert to such issues, for example if domestic violence is known to have occurred or the prospective parent discloses, or it is known that they are misusing substances in a way that is likely to significantly impact on the baby's safety or development. This is why, as stated in Chapter 3, a young mother, despite being inclusive with the father, should always be seen on her own during the antenatal and postnatal period. Concerns should be addressed as early as possible in order to provide sufficient time for full assessment and support to help enable the prospective parents to provide safe care or plan to ensure the safety of the baby following birth. It is also important to assess the safety of the young parent. Young parents can often be living with their families and may have themselves been victims of abuse in the past.

## Domestic abuse

## Domestic abuse

It is worth noting that children who are exposed to violence between adults are at an increased risk of violence themselves. Children exposed to adult violence can suffer long-term effects even if they are not caught in the crossfire of violence as these psychological and emotional effects may be similar in kind and severity to those suffered by children who are direct victims of abuse (Beckett 2007).

Children in violent households may live with intense and chronic fear of further violent incidents, including fear that the abuse will at some point be directed to them. Children may experience feelings of shame and isolation. They may feel guilt at being unable to intervene or feel too frightened to do so or feel obliged to collude with the abuse. They will have to cope with powerful emotions towards their parents/adult carers. These are all features characteristic of the effects of direct abuse and neglect (Beckett 2007).

**Good Practice Box**

It is important that those working with young fathers and their children are aware of the above indicators and warning signs in order to recognise concerns and refer these concerns to other relevant agencies. If there is a concern about actual or potential harm to a child or young person then a referral to social services must be made in accordance with the legislative framework and local policy guidance. It is important that practitioners are familiar with local Safeguarding Policies for their area.

Please note that when a concern is identified it is NOT your responsibility to diagnose the type of abuse but to share concerns and observations factually with other agencies. The nature of the abuse is determined by a multi-agency assessment through effective inter-professional and interdisciplinary working.

## The legislative framework

**Legislative framework**

The two sections of the Children Act 1989 that professionals *must* be aware of pertain to Sections 17 and 47.

**Section 17** concerns a child in need and requires local authorities to provide services for children and families in need. A child is considered to be in need if:

- he or she is unlikely to achieve or maintain, or to have the opportunity of achieving or maintaining, reasonable standard of health or development without the provision for him or her of services by a local authority;

- his or her health or development is likely to be significantly impaired, or further impaired, without the provision for him or her of such services;

- he or she is disabled, (a child is disabled if he is blind, deaf or dumb or suffers from mental disorder of any kind or is substantially and permanently handicapped by illness, injury or congenital deformity or other such disability as may be prescribed).

Section **47** of the Children Act 1989 concerns the duty of local authorities to assess and investigate situations where there are suspicions that a child has suffered significant harm (or could in the future) from lack of care or a deliberate act by her or his carers. If the child is considered to be at risk of significant harm, Section 47 of the Act provides a number of options, as follows.

## Emergency Protection Order

An **Emergency Protection Order** enables the applicant (usually social services) to remove a child to a safe environment or to prevent the removal of a child from a safe environment. The order lasts for eight days but can be challenged after 74 hours by parents/carers. However, the Court will need to be satisfied that:

- there is reasonable cause to believe that the child is likely to suffer significant harm;

- access to the child is being frustrated when the applicant has reasonable cause to believe that access is required as a matter of urgency.

The key feature is the need to balance the protection requirements of the child and the legitimate interests and responsibilities of the parents/carers.

## Child Assessment Order

A **Child Assessment Order** is a time limited order enabling social services to undertake or arrange for an assessment of a child to be undertaken without the consent of the parent or care giver. This assessment considers the child's physical, emotional and psychological well being. However, the Court needs to be satisfied that the applicant has reasonable cause to suspect the child is suffering or likely to suffer significant harm but is not at immediate risk. It is unlikely that such an assessment can be made in the absence of such an order due to lack of co-operation, and the court will not grant a Child Assessment Order if there are grounds for an Emergency Protection Order. It must be noted though that a Child Assessment Order does not permit the assessment of a mature child if he or she refuses to consent to such a medical or psychiatric examination/assessment.

## Assessment and the Common Assessment Framework

It is an accepted principle that assessment is the foundation of sound child protection work and planning. In safeguarding and promoting the welfare of children in need (or in need of protecting) it is important to ascertain whether a child is in need and how that child and family might best be helped. The effectiveness with which a child's needs are assessed will be key to subsequent actions and services and to the outcomes for the child. Thus those working with young fathers and their families need to be aware of the Common Assessment Framework which provides a common process for the early assessment to identify more accurately and speedily the additional needs of children and young people (Department for Education and Skills 2006a).

It is a framework for assessment which can be built up over time and is shared between professionals, for the ongoing assessment of all children who are vulnerable, in need and in need of protection. The framework is designed to:

- improve the quality of referrals between agencies by making the referrals more evidence based;
- help embed a common language about the needs of children and young people;
- promote the appropriate sharing of information;  and
- reduce the number and duration of the different assessment processes which children and young people need to undergo. (Department for Education and Skills 2006a).

## Professional responses: what should I do if I am concerned?

**Professional responses**

Health and social care practitioners who have concerns about young fathers and their families should:

- share concerns with relevant agencies and professionals;
- identify if the child or young father is vulnerable, in need or in need of protection from significant harm;
- decide if and what interventions can be put in place in their own agency
- decide whether there should be a Section 17 referral to social services or a Section 47 referral to social services.

If it is a Section 17 referral then the parents (or the young person themselves if it is about them instead of or as well as their child) should consent to the referral. If it is a Section 47 referral then their consent is not required. However, it is important to share and document whether or not the parents know the referral is being made. The premise is to be open and honest with parents. All actions should be in the child's best interests and if it is justified, this includes withholding information from the parents of a child where there are concerns of abuse.

All actions should be documented factually in the appropriate records for the child and/or the young father. Any concerns regarding children referred to social services should be specific in respect of any actual or potential risk. Decisions taken to implement child protection procedures may be taken on receipt of an initial referral from workers.

---

## Good Practice Box

### Those working with young fathers should:

- know where the local Safeguarding Board's manual is kept;
- have a working knowledge of local policy and what it contains;
- know whether child protection policies can be accessed on the trust intranet;
- know the local policy for triggering child protection procedures;
- have information about 'Working Together' in England and Wales or 'Protecting Children' in Scotland, and the expectation of sharing responsibility regarding the safeguarding and protecting of children by working with other agencies;
- know who the named professionals for child protection are within the organisation;
- have the ability to recognise the signs and symptoms of child abuse.

## How should you record the grounds for your concern?

**Recording concern**

Concerns should be recorded factually in the relevant records. There should be a written record of:

- discussions with the child
- discussions with the parent(s)
- discussions with managers
- information provided to Social Services
- decisions taken
- notes/records should be clearly timed, dated and signed.

Child protection policies should follow the requirements of the Human Rights Act 1998 and thus actions must have due regard to the individual's rights under the Act. Decisions and their reasons must be properly recorded at all stages of procedures or intervention.

## With whom could or should you discuss your concern within your own agency or organisation?

**Discussing concern**

Concerns should be shared with other professionals. However, a formal referral or any urgent medical treatment must not be delayed by the need for consultation. Thus, if a child is suffering from a serious injury, medical attention must be sought and social services informed. Except in cases where emergency treatment is needed, social services and the police are responsible for ensuring that any medical examinations required as part of enquiries are initiated.

Once concerns are identified it is important to make an objective assessment of:

- the needs of the child;
- whether or not the parents or carers are able to respond appropriately to the child's needs;
- whether or not the child is being adequately safeguarded from significant harm, and are the parents or carers able to promote the child's health and development;

- whether or not action is required to safeguard and promote the child's welfare;
- the reason for any referrals as either a child in need or a child in need of protection thus clarifying the source of the referral and reason;
- the information that needs to be acquired – now or during a later assessment.

It will also help to:

- explore facts and feelings;
- give meaning to the situation which distinguishes the child and family's understanding and feelings from those of the professionals;
- reach an understanding of what is happening, problems, strengths and difficulties, and the impact on the child (with the young father and/or his family wherever possible) (Webb 2007).

### Reporting your concern: to whom?

**Reporting concern**

The common route for a referral would be to a duty social worker employed by the local authority. The local authority provides social services and they are expected to co-operate in accordance with their policies and the legal framework and under the general guidance of the Secretary of State. Social services take a lead role in child protection work but rely on the co-operation of all other agencies involved. They have a statutory duty to co-ordinate and facilitate the services involved in protecting children at the initial enquiry to establish whether there are genuine concerns about a child and if so they must enable appropriate meetings with other agencies within the required time-frame. They have an obligation to keep a child at home unless there is immediate danger to the child and to provide the services necessary to achieve this.

Referrals can also be made to the police where the child is in immediate danger. The police have immediate powers and their help may be needed in acutely dangerous situations. The police are involved in child protection as part of their responsibility for the prevention and investigation of crime. They have a major role in child protection procedures. They also have emergency powers not available to other agencies. They can without prior application to the court:

- remove a child to suitable accommodation and keep them there;
- detain a child in a place of protection, for example keeping a baby in hospital and not allowing the parents to remove the child;
- enter premises to search for a child in order to save life or limb.

---

**Good Practice Box**

## Myth or fact?

Parents and others can be under the mistaken belief that social workers' main role is to remove children from the home.

This is not so, as no-one has the power to remove a child from its home or parents without a court order and those working with young fathers and their families can help to dispel this myth.

---

Any child detained in police protection can be kept in a safe place within their protection for 72 hours in England and Wales and 24 hours in Scotland. This would give social services time to obtain a court order to continue the protection of the child should this be necessary. The police would inform social services as a matter of course and the child protection processes follow the same framework whichever agency is the first point of contact (Webb 2007).

## Case Examples

1. A family support worker receives a telephone call from the father of a six-year-old boy. He informs them that his six-year-old boy has been left at home alone. The father is at work 20 miles away and he has received a telephone call from the boy's mother who has informed the father that she has done this. The father has contacted the family support worker as he is concerned and unsure what to do.

2. A young father telephones a midwife to say that he is concerned about his partner who believes that their six-week-old baby has evil spirits inside them. The father is not able to contact any friends or family to check on his partner and he is 50 miles away working.

Both of the above would be situations when it would be appropriate to contact the police in order for them to visit and assess the situation in relation to the child or baby's safety. It would also be appropriate to inform social services as well but let them know that the police have been called. The police would then have to liaise with social services but the immediate priority would be to ensure that the children are safe from harm.

### Do you have individual responsibility to make a referral?

## Making a referral

Any practitioner or member of the public can make a referral (to social services or the police depending on the context). Those working with young fathers and their families have a responsibility to refer a child to social services when it is believed or suspected that a child under the age of eighteen years or an unborn baby:

- has suffered significant harm in that the child is experiencing or may have already experienced abuse or neglect;
- is likely to suffer significant harm in the future or
- with agreement of a person with parental responsibility would be likely to benefit from family support services.

The timing of such referrals must reflect the perceived risk but should usually be within one working day of the recognition of risk. In urgent situations, out of office hours, the referral should be made to the emergency or duty social worker. At other times if the child is known to have a social worker the referral may be made directly to them. However, practitioners are advised to check their local child protection procedures.

## What will happen when I make a referral?

There is an expectation that the person making a referral will have carefully considered the information and gathered some background information before making the referral. The immediate response to referral from those working with young fathers may be:

- no further action at this stage or
- provision of services and
- a fuller initial assessment of needs within seven days or sooner if the criteria for initiating   S. 47 enquiries are met
- a core assessment may then be completed within thirty-five days if indications exist that this is required
- emergency action to protect the child
- a S. 47 strategy discussion meeting where the child and/or family are well known or the facts clearly indicate that a S. 47 enquiry is required.

If, after a referral and then the initial assessment which should be completed within seven days, it is decided that services will be provided under Section 17 of the Children Act then a lead professional will be appointed to coordinate the case and the ongoing assessment. This person will hold the Common Assessment of the Child. Social services will always lead a Section 47 case.

## Who can I share information with and what about confidentiality?

**Confidentiality**

The information that you share with other agencies must be justified in the context of child's best interests. If you can justify that at the time of your assessment there is a need to share information, then do so as long as the information you share is only relevant to the child protection issue. It is advocated that to keep children safe from harm it is essential that professionals maximise the potential to share relevant information across geographical and professional boundaries. Sharing information helps to piece the jigsaw together.

# Safeguarding young fathers and their children

The main sources of relevant law with respect to information sharing and confidentiality in child protection are:

- Common Law of Confidence
- European Convention on Human Rights (via its introduction into English law in the Human Rights Act 1998)
- Data Protection Act 1998
- Crime and Disorder Act 1998
- Children Act 1989 (Scotland 1995)
- Children Act 2004
- The Caldicot Standards (applicable to health and social services).

Guidance is available in What to Do If You are Worried a Child is Being Abused (DfES 2006b). The government has also taken powers through the Children Act 2004 to require the establishment of national standards of databases or index systems to enable professionals to identify the child or young person. Thus those working with young fathers and their families are expected to follow and use both local and national procedures for information sharing.

**NB** The Child Protection Register in its present form is going to be incorporated into the national database. The overall legal position is that in general the law does not prevent individual sharing of information with other professionals if:

- those likely to be affected consent;
- the public interest in safeguarding the child's welfare overrides the need to keep information confidential;
- disclosure is required under a court order or other legal obligation.

When in doubt practitioners are advised to seek advice from the relevant personnel within the organisation.

---

### Good Practice Box

The Child Protection Register does not protect the child. It is the actions and interventions of the professionals that give protection.

---

## Conclusions

Safeguarding the welfare of children and young people of all ages can be challenging and the phenomena of abuse and neglect are complex. It is, however, important that those working with young fathers and their children have an understanding of what constitutes harm and that they are able to recognise not only harm but vulnerabilities that may increase the risk of harm or abuse to the child. It is important to recognise that not all risk factors will lead to the abuse of a child but if a child is vulnerable then it is important that the vulnerabilities are recognised so that interventions are put in place. These interventions such as family or parenting support may be enough to improve the outcomes for a family and offset the need for child protection procedures. However, if there are concerns that a child has been harmed as a result of abuse or neglect then child protection procedures are essential. Situations and social context that make a young father vulnerable are discussed further in Chapter 7. This chapter has discussed what constitutes a vulnerable child, harm and the definitions of abuse. Situations that raise concerns about a child's welfare have been identified, as have the specific indicators of abuse. Assessment, however, is a joint responsibility irrespective of who is coordinating the case.

In the first instance it is important that practitioners are able to recognise concerns and know what to do. This chapter has provided this guidance in accordance with legislation and policy for practice.

### Key messages

- The welfare of the child and or young person is paramount.
- It is important to recognise and respond to concerns about the welfare of a child or young person whether they are vulnerable and in need or vulnerable and in need of protection.
- Do not dismiss concerns.
- Concerns must be shared with other professionals.
- A named Child Protection Advisor is available to offer guidance within your own organisation or within an identified agency.
- All concerns and actions must be recorded.

# Safeguarding young fathers and their children

- Guidance must be sought through local agency guidelines and in collaboration with other agencies.
- Refer to the Local Safeguarding Board's Multi-Agency policy and other guidelines for protecting children and young people.
- It is important to know where the local policy and procedures are located.
- Child protection is not the responsibility of a single agency. Multi-agency working is essential and the practice of safe-guarding children and young people is dependent on inter-disciplinary and inter-professional working.
- Always seek personal support.
(Webb 2007)

## References

Beckett, C. (2007). *Child Protection an Introduction* 2nd edn. London: Sage Publications

Belsky, J. (1993). 'Etiology of child maltreatment: A developmental-ecological analysis' in *Psychological Bulletin* 114: 413–434.

Bergner, R.M., Delgado, L.K. & Graybill, D. (1994). 'Finkelhor's risk factor checklist: a cross validation study' in *Child Abuse and Neglect* 18 (4): 331–340.

Browne, K. & Stevenson, O. (1988). A Checklist for completion by health visitors to identify children 'at risk' for child abuse. Report to the Surrey Area Review Committee on Child Abuse (unpublished). In Browne, K., Davies, C. & Stratton, P. (eds) *Early Prediction and Prevention of Child Abuse.* Wiley: Chichester.

Browne, K.D. & Herbert, M. (1997). *Preventing Family Violence*. Chichester: Wiley.

Browne, K. (2002). 'Child abuse: Defining, understanding and intervening' in Wilson, K. & James, A. (eds) *The Child Protection Handbook* 2nd edn. London: Bailliere Tindall.

Chase, E., Knight, A. & Warwick, I. (2005). 'Rescue remedies' in *Community Care* 20-26th May: 40–41.

Cleaver, H., Unell, I. & Aldgate, J. (1999). *Children's Needs – Parenting Capacity: The Impact of Parental Illness, Problem Alcohol and Drug Use, and Domestic Violence on Children's Development*. London: The Stationery Office.

Corby, B. (2006). *Child Abuse: Towards a Knowledge Base* 3rd edn. Berkshire: Open University Press.

Daniel, B., Wassell, S. & Gilligan, R. (1999). *Child Development for Child Care and Protection Workers*. London: Jessica Kingsley.

Department for Education and Skills (2003). *Every Child Matters*. London: The Stationery Office (on line at www.dfes.gov.uk/everychildmatters).

Department for Education and Skills (2006a). *The Common Assessment Framework*. London: The Stationery Office.

Department for Education and Skills (2006b). *What to Do If You are Worried a Child is Being Abused*. London: The Stationery Office.

Department of Health (1991). *The Children Act 1989 Guidance and Regulations Volume 1 Court Orders*. London: HMSO.

Department of Health (1995a). *Child Protection – Messages from Research*. London: HMSO.

Department of Health (1995b). *A Guide for Guardians ad Litem in Public Law Proceedings under the Children Act 1989*. London: HMSO.

Department of Health (2000) *Framework for the Assessment of Children in Need and their Families*. London: The Stationery Office.

Department of Health (2004). *The National Service Framework for Children, Young People and Maternity Services*. London: DoH (online at www.publications.doh.gov.uk/nsf/children).

Dimond, B. (2002). *Legal Aspects of Midwifery* 2nd edn. Oxford: Books for Midwives Press.

Dubowitz, H. (1989). 'Prevention of child maltreatment: What is known' in *Pediatrics* 83: 570–577.

Ennals, P., Bernard, J., Davies, O., Bullock, R. & Tunstill, J. (2003). *'The will is there, but is the money? What do the proposals in the green paper on children "Every Child Matters" mean for the professionals who will be charged with putting them into practice? Our team of experts assess the likely impact'*. Online at www.communitycare.co.uk September 14 2003.

Gordon, R. & Harran, E. (2001). *Fragile: Handle with Care: Protecting Babies from Harm*. Leicester: NSPCC.

Greenland, C. (1987). *Preventing CAN Deaths: An International Study of Deaths due to Child Abuse and Neglect*. London: Tavistock.

HM Government (2006). *Working Together to Safeguard Children: A Guide to Interagency Working to Safeguard and Promote the Welfare of Children*. London: The Stationery Office.

Howard, P. (2004). Foreword in Fraser, J. & Nolan, M. (2004). *Child Protection: A Guide for Midwives*. London: BFM

Lord Laming (2003). *The Victoria Climbié Inquiry Report*. London: The Stationery Office.

Parliament (1984). *The Matrimonial and Family Proceedings Act*. London: HMSO.

Parliament (1989). *Children Act 1989*. London: HMSO.

Parliament (1991a). *The Child Support Act*. London: HMSO.

Parliament (1991b). *Criminal Justice Act, 1991*. London: HMSO.

Parliament (1998). *The Human Rights Act*. London: HMSO.

Parliament (2002). *Adoption and Children Act 2002*. London: TSO.

Parliament (2004). *Children Act 2004*. London: TSO.

Pearce, J. (2003). 'Parental mental health and child protection' in *Child Abuse Review* 12(2): 114–118.

Powell, C. (2003). 'Early indicators of child abuse and neglect: A multi-professional delphi study' in *Child Abuse Review* 12: 25–40.

Reeves, J. (2006). *'You've got to keep your head on' A study of the stories young male service users tell about the transition to fatherhood*. Unpublished thesis: The Open University.

Scottish Executive (2002). *'It's everyone's job to make sure I'm alright' Report of the Child Protection Audit and Review*. Edinburgh: Scottish Executive.

Thyen, U., Thiessen, R. & Heinsohn-Krug, M. (1995). 'Secondary prevention: serving families at risk' in *Abuse and Neglect* 19: 1337–1347.

Webb, J. (2007). 'Safeguarding and protecting children' in Cleaver, K. & Webb, J. *Emergency Care of Children and Young People*. Oxford: Blackwell Publishing.

Wright, D. (2002). 'We can't do it alone' in *Community Care* 41. www.community-care.co.uk 25 April–1 May 2002.

# Chapter 6
# The role of fathers in their children's lives
**Rosa Panades-Blas**

## Introduction

The nature of the roles that fathers play in their children's lives is of much interest to researchers, policy makers and professionals (Henwood & Procter 2003) with literature on the subject substantially expanding over the last 15 to 20 years (Drape 2003, Matta & Knudson-Martin 2006). Generally, as mentioned in Chapter 1, most conceptualisations and research on fatherhood are based on a dichotomy between the role of the economic provider, following the male breadwinner family model (Lewis 2001), and the role of the carer (Matta & Knudson-Martin 2006, Smith *et al.* 2007), which is also referred to in the fatherhood literature as the 'nurturing male' (Matta & Knudson-Martin 2006), 'modern fatherhood' (Smith *et al.* 2007), 'hands-on-fathering' (Brannen & Nielsen 2006) or 'new fatherhood' (Henwood & Procter 2003) amongst others.

The purpose of this chapter is to broaden the discussion on young fathers to look at the influences on their relationships with their child(ren). The chapter firstly introduces debates surrounding the provider and carer roles in contemporary fatherhood. Secondly, it attempts to situate changes in fatherhood practices within the realm of family change. This leads to a third section on lone motherhood and teenage motherhood, followed by the introduction of social exclusion theory, and the place of teenage parenthood in it. We then go on to discuss discourse theory and its possible effects on how professionals work with young fathers. Following these sections, we focus on young fatherhood, initially looking at the way in which the role of young fathers may be affected by expectations of being both the breadwinner and fulfilling the carer role. Secondly, we move away from the economic provider debates to explore specific influence on the young father's role, such as stress theory and the father-mother relationship. Thirdly, the focus is on the specific contributions that young fathers make to their children's lives. Finally, the role of the father's involvement generally is reviewed, with special attention to one aspect: play. This is followed by a section on the role of play in father–child attachment. The chapter concludes with a model of the potential influences on young fathers' role that need to be assessed when working with them.

## Changing roles, changing relationships? Key debates in fatherhood

**Changing roles**

Contemporary discussions about fatherhood and the relationships that fathers have with their children seem to revolve around the role of breadwinner vs. that of carer. Discourses of 'new fatherhood' argue that the role of the father as sole or main breadwinner is diminishing and that the role of the carer is gaining centre stage (Tyrer *et al.* 2005, Featherstone 2003). However, it appears that 'the role of the economic provider continues to be a central aspect of father's identity' (Featherstone 2003: 240). It can be said that this duality of roles underlies most of the issues dealt with in this chapter, mainly due to its impact on theories, conceptualisation and perceptions of fatherhood. Smith *et al.* (2007: 1) argue that 'a common conception of modern fatherhood is that there has to be a trade off between being a financial provider or an active carer'; this implies that the role of the provider and the role of the carer are seen as mutually incompatible. However, the dichotomy between the provider father and the caring one, in which one role excludes the other, may not be a good representation of 'new fatherhood' as the complexity and intricacies of the issue are then lost (Matta & Knudson-Martin 2006, Smith *et al.* 2007). Similarly, Henwood & Procter (2003: 337) state that 'neither "hegemonic masculinity" nor the "men as part of the family" perspectives exhaust the options for reading the gratifications and tensions advanced in men's accounts of living contemporary fatherhood'. It seems that one of the changes in contemporary fatherhood practice is that a great number of fathers are no longer sole breadwinners, which has brought about a cultural change in the sense 'bread-winning is no longer seen to legitimize a form of fathering whereby men are exempt from active involvement with children' (Brannen & Nielsen 2006: 348). In short, contemporary fathers cannot be seen as either super-dads or absentee dads (Lewis & Warin 2001). For this reason, it is important to acknowledge the multi-faceted roles that fathers can play in their children's lives.

## Families and fathers: a contemporary snapshot

**Families and fathers**

It is significant to note the diversification in patterns of living arrangements for fathers (Reeves 2003):

- Fathers living with all and only their own biological children in partnership with the children's biological mother
- Living as a lone father with his own children
- Living in partnership, not with the biological mother, but with some or all of his biological children
- Father not living with any biological children
- Living in partnership with children that are not his
- Father living on his own with some of his biological children
- Living in a partnership with a combination of children from previous relationships
- Living just with step children
- Living with additional biological children from a current relationship.

Indeed, the role of fathers has generally been affected by contemporary changes in family practices and forms.

## Family changes

**Family changes**

The decline of the traditional nuclear family, composed of a married heterosexual couple with a male breadwinner head of the household, is central to contemporary anxieties surrounding family debates amongst academics, politicians and the media (Lewis 2001). Although the two-parent, married couple family continues to be the most popular family type, latest statistics show a 4% decline of this family form between 1996 and 2006, despite an overall 4% increase in the number of families (ONS 2007). Debates surrounding the decline of the nuclear family are fed not only by the decrease of marriage, but also by the increase of cohabiting families which grew by over 60% between 1996 and 2006 and of lone mother families, which increased by 11% between those years (ONS 2007). In 2006 nine out of ten children living in single parent households lived with their mother (ONS 2007). Lone father families represent 2% of all single-headed families, a figure that has remained consistent between 1996 and 2006 (ONS 2007).

## Changing family forms and the role of the father

**Changing family forms**

It is partly due to this diversity of family forms, that it is argued that the role of fathers is not as straightforward as it once was (Featherstone 2003). This may be particularly true of young fathers, who are less likely to live with the mother of their child (Pears *et al.* 2005), but who, as evolving research suggests, may nevertheless be involved in some way. Indeed, as Marsiglio *et al.* (2000: 1175) point out 'the growing diversity of life course and residency patterns of men and children today... need to be recognised when conceptualisations of paternal involvement are broadened'. This idea may be particularly pertinent to those working with young fathers, not only in terms of acknowledging their potential contributions but also in finding young fathers' strengths and thinking creatively about the role young fathers, resident or non-resident, can be encouraged to play.

Another aspect of the debate is the growing number of children born outside marriage. Around 42% of births in England and Wales are to unmarried parents, 68% of which are cohabiting. A total of 27% of children are born outside marriage (ONS 2005). Moreover, concerns are based on the reported greater fragility of cohabiting couples compared to married ones (Lewis *et al.* 2002). It is estimated that 65% of children of cohabiting unions will experience their parents' break-up before they reach 16 years old, as opposed to 30% of children of married couples (Ermisch & Francesconi 2000).

# The role of fathers in their children's lives

## Bringing home the bread?

**The breadwinner**

That the role of the breadwinner is still prominent in fathers' lives is not, in some ways, surprising given that, despite the fact that the number of working mothers has increased, those with children under five have the lowest rate of employment, with 32%, compared to those with no dependent children, with 58% (ONS 2002). Also, research shows that on average, fathers earn two-thirds of the family income (Lewis & Warin 2001); consequently a father's work is closely linked to breadwinning responsibilities, compared to that of mothers since his employment remains continuous and full-time (Brannen & Nielsen 2006).

Thus, employment, just like family form, appears to impact on the father role on a number of levels. For example, work impacts on the time that fathers spend caring for their children (Smith *et al.* 2007):

- Fathers who earn more, also dedicate more time to caring for their children.
- Fathers who work shorter hours spend more time caring for their children.
- Of all fathers, those whose partners work spend the most time looking after their children.

Fathers' work is thus likely to dictate the available time that fathers have for their children, not only in relation to care but also in terms of leisure and play (Beets *et al.* 2007). Clearly time is an issue to bear in mind when assessing the level and type of involvement that young fathers can make to their children's lives. Also, work, or the lack of it, can have an impact in the attitude of fathers towards their children. Indeed, it is argued that there may be some differences amongst fatherhood practices in relation to the socio-economic position of fathers:

- Changes in the labour market have hit hardest working class fathers, as 'the decline in manual jobs, specially unskilled work, has eroded the employment opportunities of some working-class men and limited their potential to be "providers"' (Brannen & Nielsen 2006: 306).
- Golombok (2000: 22) argues, when fathers are 'forced' to enter the caring role by, for example, becoming unemployed, their

approach to being involved and their impact may not be as positive as that of fathers who chose their involvement.

## Perspectives on lone motherhood

**Lone motherhood**

Another aspect of family change is the aforementioned increase in numbers of families headed by a lone mother. As Lewis (2001: 161) points out: 'In large measure, late twentieth century pessimism about the family has been a reaction to the scale and rapidity of the changes in the demographic statistics, which have produced a rethink of divorce and lone motherhood.' Lone motherhood was clearly in focus during the 1990s, and during this time 'these women were vilified as both a problem and a threat to the traditional nuclear family and to the nation' (Carabine 2001: 271). To some extent, it can be argued that some contemporary debates surrounding lone motherhood have taken some emphasis away from the 'lone mother', and placed it instead on the 'absent father'. (This is not to say that lone mothers are not still at the centre of the debate or have been completely disregarded.) The mentioning, or blaming, of absent fathers is not new. Charles Murray's 1990s underclass critique of lone mothers 'is based on the undesirable effects on children and on the community on the absence of fathers' (Murray 1996: 62). In this sense, 'fatherless families' is not a completely new approach, but one that is being revived in the current socio-political arena of the late 2000s. The consequences of growing up without a father have shaped the way that policy makers and researchers approach the issues that concern fathers and families (Marsiglio *et al.* 2000).

It is important to remember that one cannot equate 'lone mother' with 'teenage mother', as there are different routes by which women become lone mothers, see Figure 6.1. Although some may have none or little involvement with the father from the start, or from very early on, others may be alone as a result of divorce, separation or death of the partner. However, part of the debate surrounding lone motherhood is directly related to teenage motherhood because teenage relationships are characterised by instability which means that most teenage mothers will eventually become lone mothers. Statistics show that 90% of births to young women under 20 occur outside marriage (ONS 2005). However,

# The role of fathers in their children's lives

there is an indication that a significant number of fathers are initially acknowledged, as 74% of all teenage births outside marriage were jointly registered by the couple, and 54% of those are registered as living in the same address (ONS 2005). The overall rate for births outside marriage jointly registered as living at the same address in England and Wales is 74% (ONS 2005). Teenage motherhood is therefore seen as a social problem because it is regarded as an indicator of the demise of the traditional nuclear family (Duncan 2007) and the aforementioned fatherless families. Moreover, teenage pregnancy is seen as a problem because it often leads to unsupported motherhood (Bonnell 2004).

**Figure 6.1**    **Routes into and out of single parenthood**

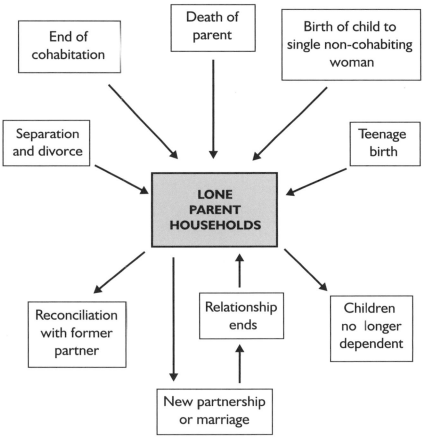

(Source: Reeves 2003: 6)

# Inter-professional approaches to young fathers

## Thinking about teenage mothers

There is evidence that not all young women are equally vulnerable to becoming teenage mothers. A number of factors have been found to be at play in putting some teenagers at a higher risk than others, which are similar to those of young men: poverty, lack of education and being the offspring of a teenage mother (SEU 1999, Swann *et al*. 2003). It is also well documented that becoming a mother at a young age can have a negative impact on young women's health, as well as hindering education and career prospects. Moreover, generally, children of teenage mothers fare worse in life than those of older mothers (DfES 2006, SEU 1999, Swann *et al*. 2003).

Teenage mothers have now been identified as a group with needs to be addressed (Tabberer *et al*. 2000) and new initiatives to reduce teenage conceptions have been put into place. These include better support in preventing teenage pregnancy through increasing sex and relationship education as well as by improving information and access to contraception. Also, increased support for teenage mothers, to ensure they finish education and learn parenting skills is being introduced (SEU 1999).

Identifying those young women who are at a higher risk of mothering a child is crucial in order for these initiatives to have an impact and decrease teenage birth rates. However, 'for many young mothers and fathers, parenting seems to provide the impetus to change direction, or build on existing resources' (Duncan 2007: 3), and the focus on reduction, which stems from problematising teenage pregnancy, will be dealt with later in the chapter.

## Social exclusion perspective

One of the reasons for which fatherless families, and particularly young families, are of concern is that lone teenage mothers, particularly working class lone mothers, are more likely to suffer social exclusion, which in turn has a potential negative effect on the children's development and future chances (Rowlingson & McKay 2005). The social exclusion perspective focuses on teenage parenthood. This perspective suggests that a cycle of deprivation is created, in which children who are born to deprived families, or communities affected by disadvantage, are more likely to remain in this disadvantaged position and hand it down to subsequent generations (Social Exclusion Task Force 2006). Thus, the new Social Exclusion Task Force (SETF), set up in 2006, which replaced the Social Exclusion Unit created in 1997 (both put into place by the Labour government) believe that 'cycles of disadvantage can be broken. It is possible to mitigate the life-long effects of social exclusion and prevent them from being passed down to future generations. Key to this is providing early and appropriate support' (SETF 2006: 7).

The paradox with young fathers is that in the debate surrounding 'absent fathers', many of them would fit into it as both 'victims' of fatherless families as well as current or future 'perpetrators' of such a family type. Indeed, research shows young fathers are less likely to have lived with both natural parents (Quinton *et al.* 2002) and not to have had a stable father figure through their lives (Tan & Quinlivan 2006). Although there is no statistical data for the UK that shows exactly how many young fathers are there, how trends may have changed over the years and how many maintain contact with their children (Sheriff 2007), qualitative studies show that young fathers face particular difficulties in keeping relationships with their sons and daughters (Speak *et al.* 1997). This would point to their greater chance to create a fatherless family. Not offering or providing support for young fathers may thus mean that the cycle of disadvantage is not broken.

## Young parents and social exclusion

**Young parents and exclusion**

There are different hypotheses as to why young fathers, as well as young mothers, are more likely to be socially excluded. One is that 'the roots of social exclusion for young parents lie in poverty and deprivation, not in early parenthood *per se*' (Higginbottom *et al.* 2006: 859). Thus, young men become young dads because they are socially excluded, rather than becoming socially excluded because they become young fathers (Duncan 2007). This points to the need for prevention work and early intervention with young fathers. Also, there is the possibility that young fathers are more likely to be socially excluded because young parenthood disrupts their pathway into education and employment (Sigle-Rushton 2005), implying a need to offer support and training in skills and education.

## Case Scenario

Jake is 19 and he first became a father when he was 16, having been with his girlfriend for two years. He now has two children aged three and one. He was living with his girlfriend and her mother from the age of 15, as his mum 'kicked him out' of the house because 'he was getting into trouble'. Jake left school with three GSCEs and wanted to become a car mechanic. However, when he found out he was to become a father, he started working because he needed to support his new family. A year and a half later he and his partner had a further child and as a result, Jake had to further postpone enrolling in his course and continued working. Having found out about a new paid apprentice mechanic course, he is now due to start his studies next year. Even though the apprenticeship will bring a bit less money home, he will still be able to support his family while fulfilling his desire to become a car mechanic.

Issues of social exclusion are of particular importance to practice and to those professionals involved with young fathers. Although it is now generally agreed that fathers do make positive contributions to their children's development (Sheriff 2007), due to the greater risk of social exclusion and disadvantage that young fathers may have been subjected to, it cannot be assumed that their involvement in their children's lives will always be beneficial. Thus 'characteristics that would interfere with healthy and effective parenting or a father's ability to provide for his child should be considered and addressed in programs that seek to increase the involvement of young fathers with their children' (Sigle-Rushton 2005: 749). It can be argued that without the appropriate support, this will affect the role they play and the relationship they develop with their child.

---

**Good Practice Box**

**Working with fatherless fathers**

1. Inquire about whom they lived with in childhood.
2. Were there consistent figures in their childhood?
3. How deprived or socially excluded was their childhood?
4. Are they receiving any support from their father or father figure?
5. After assessing their situation according to the points above, think creatively of ways of helping – such as counselling, fatherhood groups, fatherhood organisations and so on.
6. Offer the appropriate source of help and encourage take-up.

---

## Discourse theory and its influence on the 'reality' of being a young father

**Discourse theory**

Representations of teenage parents generally and young fathers specifically in the media, popular culture or in academic research can be conceptualised as 'discourses'. There is an array of definitions in the literature on discourse (Phillips & Hardy 2002) but it is not the intention of this section to offer an exhaustive review of definitions. Here, we will concentrate on the work of the French thinker Foucault, who according to Hall (2001: 72) 'gave it [discourse] a different meaning'. Discourse is generally used as a linguistic term, related to the activities of writing and talking (Hall 2001, Phillips & Hardy 2002), however, Foucault broke the traditional linguistic divide between language and practice. To him,

> discourse . . . constructs the topic. It defines and produces the objects of our knowledge. It governs the way that a topic can be meaningfully talked about and reasoned about. It also influences how ideas are put into practice and used to regulate the conduct of others. (Hall 2001: 72)

In this sense, as argued by Carabine (2001), the relevance of discourses lay in the fact that they are 'productive'. Indeed, discourses create the object of which they speak – in this case, young fatherhood – and create a version of it that is presented as 'real' or 'true'. The idea is that some discourses acquire the authority necessary to have 'truth' value, but this truth is an abstract element, not a real material one (Hacking 1998: 35). Thus, if the common view, or discourse, about young fathers as disinterested affects the way that these dads are treated, either in practice or policy, then it can be said that a discourse has acquired a certain status of 'truth'. It is therefore important to look at the ways standard discourse can structure social issues:

- In relation to professional practice, there is evidence that young fathers receive little support and preparation in the transition to parenthood and are not encouraged to play a role in their children's lives (Quinton et al. 2002, Speak et al. 1997, Tyrer et al. 2005).

- Studies on services that have an involvement in young men's lives show that fathers are often ignored or marginalised and their roles and capabilities may be undermined, even when they show interest in information, advice or inclusion (Quinton et al. 2002). A recent study revealed service providers did not know whether the young men they supported were fathers and they did not see their roles as supporting that aspect of the men's lives (Tyrer et al. 2005).

To relate discourse theory to teenage pregnancy, we can start by stating that young parenthood has not always been regarded as a problem and it still is not in some countries or in some communities, cultures or ethnic groups within Britain as well as abroad (Bonnell 2004, Coin de Carvalho 2007, Edin & Kefalas 2005, Higginbottom et al. 2006). Similarly, it can be said that the notion of young fatherhood is socially constructed and that what is regarded as young fatherhood in one country or culture may not be in another (Higginbottom et al. 2006). This is one of the issues to take into consideration with regard to the policies that are being implemented by the current Labour government, who, since the late 1990s, have aimed to reduce teenage pregnancy. As Chapter 1 has highlighted there is now more emphasis on supporting young parents and their children, and for the first time, specific guidance on young fathers has been given (DCSF 2007). A study concerned with black minority ethnic (BME) young parents found that professionals thought that too much emphasis on prevention created tensions and that there had to be a balance between supporting young parents and prevention work. Amongst some BME groups, young parenthood is often not regarded a problem but as 'normal', or common practice (Higginbottom *et al.* 2006). As Jones (2003: 23) explains: 'The problem for young people is that society seems to define some patterns of transition as inappropriate and then condemn them, even though they may be based on long-standing class or cultural traditions.'

---

**Good Practice Box**

## Thinking about professional discourses

Discourse, then, can be useful when thinking about young fathers and what is expected of them.

a. Discourse theory explains how we construct or produce concepts, and this is reflected in the many political, social or cultural views on young parenthood that exist.

b. Most relevant for this book is the way in which these views, in turn, may affect the way that professionals work with young fathers. Acknowledging and reflecting how views and representations of young fathers, or 'stereotypes', affect how young fathers are treated in practice may help professionals to develop a more open and responsive way to work with this group. This in turn may help them encourage and assist fathers to establish and maintain a relationship with their children.

---

This perspective is related to Figure 6.2, the Cycle of Exclusion Model, in which the interaction between professional and young fathers is represented. It shows how issues like lack of eye contact and communication from professionals to young fathers can make them feel alienated and marginal to their children's upbringing. As a result, they are more likely to withdraw during visits, reinforcing the stereotypical view of disinterest, and further affecting the way in which the professionals treat the young fathers. This may lead to an absence of fathers from service visits, which would mean that professionals would stop being exposed to them, consequently contributing to professional insecurities about dealing with young fathers, and seeing them as peripheral to the child's life.

**Figure 6.2**   **Cycle of exclusion model**

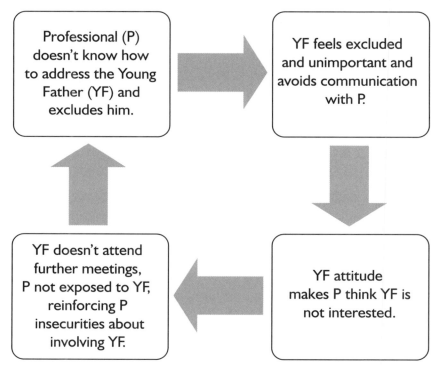

## Influences on young fathers

**Influences on young fathers**

There is little statistical information on single, non-married young fathers, and about how many maintain a relationship with their children (Speak *et al.* 1997). However, one of the reasons for the growing interest in teenage fathers is the evidence that as time passes (Quinton *et al.* 2002), the contact as well as the time spent with their children is more likely to decrease. Marriage is also a crucial factor, with Fagan & Bernd (2007: 2) suggesting that 'never married adolescent fathers are even less likely than older divorced or separated fathers to spend time with their children'. So what are the influences on the young men's roles?

## Young fathers as providers

**Young fathers as providers**

As contemporary discourses about fatherhood are based on the dichotomy between caring and providing, it is important to highlight that for men who become fathers at a young age, both roles may be difficult to fulfil. On one hand, their disadvantaged background means that they are more likely to be unemployed or underemployed. On the other, they face numerous difficulties to develop and sustain a parental role. In general terms, changes in the labour market have negatively affected young, working-class men's transition to employment and adulthood (Nayak 2006), and also their ability to fulfil the breadwinning role attached to fatherhood. The importance of traditional working-class, industrial employment is that it has: 'accrued its own type of "body capital", forged through notions of the patriarchal "breadwinner", physical "hardness" and a strict sexual division of labour that split the public "masculine" world of work from the private domestic realm of women's unpaid labour' (Nayak 2006: 814).

The situation, then, for some young fathers resembles that of some older working-class fathers, for whom the role of the breadwinner may be at odds with their financial situation and employment prospects. As explained earlier, the majority of young fathers have few educational qualifications, and, thus, poor employability (SEU 1999). Consequently, being the economic provider in a family may be a difficult role to perform by young fathers as they 'may have fewer social and economic resources available for their children or for the mother of their children' (Sigle-Rushton 2005: 1). Despite this, young men are not exempt from social expectations regarding breadwinning practices as culturally there is still a belief that a father should provide for his child, regardless of his age (Gavin *et al.* 2002).

It seems that cultural and normative expectations permeate young men's attitudes and beliefs towards fathers' responsibilities. There is a suggestion that the role of the economic provider is regarded as important by young fathers themselves, and that it can play an important role in determining father–child contact. As Bunting and McAuley (2004) argue: 'the role of the financial provider may be crucial to teenage fathers' perceptions of fatherhood and that lack of money may lead to disinterest and un-involvement in other aspects of fatherhood' (p. 299).

# Inter-professional approaches to young fathers

Recent findings suggest that young fathers who are able to financially provide for their children are also more likely to be involved (Fagan & Bernd 2007), pointing at the connection between work and father involvement. The link between lack of money and distancing from the child may lie in parenting stress, which will be explored later in this chapter. Lack of employment and financial pressures are among the main issues that young fathers have to deal with (Bunting & McAuley 2004).

The importance of employment in young fathers' involvement may also be related to the influence it exerts on the mother's view about the father and on her 'gatekeeper' role. It is not clear, however, whether young mothers place as much importance on fathers' employment and income as may be thought. While it is suggested that employment is seen by young mothers as making the young man a 'better' father (Fagan & Bernd 2007), a small-scale study based in Northern Ireland found that mothers put more emphasis on the father's help with daily caring tasks than on economic provision (Bunting & McAuley 2004).

The traditional hegemonic position of the breadwinner means that 'the definition of involvement often focuses on financial contribution, with limited attention to other dimensions of father involvement' (Gavin *et al.* 2002: 267). While the importance of economic responsibility and its potential positive effect on the father–child relationship cannot be denied, it is also true that not all young fathers will be able and ready to embrace the breadwinner role. Can young fathers provide an example of alternative ways to father? The next section will explore this.

## Young fathers: alternative ways to father?

**Alternative ways to father**

It can be argued that young fathers' unemployed status may mean that they can be involved in their children's lives in a different way to their own fathers. Indeed, this view could encourage the role of the carer as one that young fathers can take, thus contributing to their children's lives in a more practical way. Indeed, their lack of set work may entail greater flexibility to get involved in other tasks such as taking the child to the doctor or babysitting if the mother goes to school or work (Tyrer *et al.* 2005). Generally, research shows that young men are increasingly involved in their children's lives (Reeves 2006, Sheriff 2007, Speak *et al.* 1997).

In some way, this point fits with public and social perceptions of 'new fatherhood', in which the role of the carer takes centre stage and the role of the provider gets relegated to a secondary position (Tyrer *et al.* 2005). A study conducted with young men who had 'planned' the birth of their children suggested that the men's main worry was not necessarily their inability to provide economically for their children, but not 'being there' for them. The authors explain that this may be 'because they themselves were not used to having lots of material things. However, they were used to a lack of love and more specifically, the lack of a father' (Cater & Coleman 2006: 50).

Non-residence may affect the way in which a young father can care for his child, but this finding is not yet conclusive (Bunting & McAuley 2004). A UK study that included both resident and non-resident young fathers suggests that residency status may be less influential than other factors in determining young fathers' care giving and involvement (Fagan & Bernd 2007).

## Fast-track transition to fatherhood

**Transition to fatherhood**

'So how did you feel when you first saw her [daughter]?'
'Glad, I did feel happy when I see [sic] her. Well good.'
Keith, aged 19.

As Chapter 3 explored, despite initial keenness in the pregnancy and birth to be an active father, forming and maintaining a relationship with the child, or simply playing a role, can prove to be a long and difficult process for most young men and is often dependent upon their long-term relationship with their partner and wider kin networks (Reeves 2006). Young fathers' parenting role is shaped by the difficulties and hurdles they encounter, which are often related to their socially excluded background. Indeed, studies demonstrate that becoming a young parent is seen as a fast track to adulthood (Jones 2003).

Fast-track transitions, as opposed to slow-track ones, are characterised by leaving school early, coupled with and augmenting the risk of unemployment or underemployment as well as forming a family early (SEU 2005). Thus, young fathers' accelerated transition into family formation is often married to other features of fast transitions, such as having few educational qualifications (Wellings *et al.* 2001) and suffering unemployment (Speak *et al.* 1997). Added to this, there is a greater chance that young dads will be benefit-reliant (Allen & Dowling 1998, SEU 1999) as well as suffering poor mental health (Simms & Smith 1986). They are also more likely to be young offenders (Tyrer *et al.* 2005).

Consequently, one of the main problems with young fatherhood is that the young men are often unprepared to assume or tackle the responsibilities that fatherhood brings (Fagan & Bernd 2007). Moreover, Quinlivan and Condon (2005: 928) explain that young dads have been found to be more idealistic than mothers, and to underestimate the negative consequences of bearing a child and overestimate the positive ones, which often means that when faced 'with the reality of an actual pregnancy, disillusion may emerge, which may contribute to depression and anxiety'.

## Stress theory

**Stress theory**

Depression and anxiety can also be a big influence on parental involvement amongst young fathers. According to stress theory: 'parental functioning is affected by the stresses and supports experienced by parents. Stresses are likely to have an adverse effect while support has a buffering influence on the parent-child relationship' (Fagan & Bernd 2007: 2). Young fathers' parenting stress can be seen as a result of the aforementioned negative aspects of most young fathers' backgrounds and their fast-track transitions.

### Stress theory and young fathers

Stress theory states that the parenting function is affected by stresses that parents have in their lives, such as health, lack of competences and depression amongst others. In this sense, a combination of their lack of readiness to embrace parental responsibilities, coupled with the possible increased risk of depression when they try to, as well as their more idealistic approach to parenthood means that young fathers are at a greater risk of suffering from parenting stress. Parenting stress in turn has potential detrimental consequences for paternal involvement; and for young fathers this is aggravated by their reduced chances of having resources to buffer those stresses (Fagan & Bernd 2007). On top of parenting stress, father involvement and behaviour is also influenced by the father's own characteristics (personality, attitudes) and contextual sources of stress, which include the aforementioned socially excluded background as well as mother-father relationships.

One other aspect that affects father involvement that has received little attention is the characteristics of the child, such as their temperament and age (McBride *et al.* 2002, referring to Belsky 1984: 999). It is argued that a negative cycle can be created in which child characteristics add to parenting stress. Parenting stress negatively affects parenting involvement, further aggravating the child's difficult or challenging behaviour (Fagan & Bernd 2007). Child characteristics should therefore be taken into account when assessing the level of stress that a father is undergoing, as he may find it hard to cope with having a girl, an excessive crying baby or a bad sleeper, for example. If the parenting stress is not recognised and tackled, there is a great chance that it will result in the father's withdrawal from the child's life.

Such an outcome, their eventual detachment from their children's lives, would fit with stereotypical, widespread images associated with young fathers, who are often seen as detached and not involved (Hudson & Ineichen 1991). However, these negative images are not in accord with attitudes that some young men have expressed to researchers. Stein (1997) found that many young non-resident fathers, when questioned about what they saw their fathering roles to be, responded 'being there', as did young fathers who had planned the birth of their child (Cater & Coleman 2006). Such expression was also widely used by older men in a study concerned with the transition to fatherhood when they were asked what a 'good father' consisted of (Barclay & Lupton 1999). The expression 'being there', therefore, may be taken as young fathers' desire to play a role in their children's lives.

## Case Scenario

Mark is 20 years old and has a 3-year-old daughter. He had only known his girlfriend for 4 months when she became pregnant. Having grown up without a father, he wanted to 'be there' for his daughter, and decided to move in with his girlfriend soon after the birth. Not long after, however, the arguments started, and Mark moved out of their home. He thought that it would be better for them to live apart, because everything had happened so quickly that, even though they had a child together, they had not had time to get to know each other. He thought that carrying on cohabiting would have damaged the relationship, and his chance of forming a family with his girlfriend destroyed. He does not want to have children with anyone else, and does not want his daughter to be looked after by another man. Mark is now at university, and when he has finished he would like to move back in with his partner and his daughter. He feels that his decisions have been made in order to 'be there' for her and the children in the long term.

**Good Practice Box**

**Recognising stress**

Inquire about worries, including:

1. Financial worries
2. Do they need practical help gaining improved qualifications or employment?
3. Can Connexions help?
4. What are the characteristics of their relationship with their partner?
5. How are they getting on with their child?
6. Identify sources of informal/formal support.

### Lack of male role models for young fathers

**Lack of male role models**

'He used to go to work at about 6–7 am and if I was lucky he would get home at about 8 pm. So I didn't see him in the morning and didn't see him at night, because I was always asleep when he got in.' Manuel, in Reeves 2006.

It is known that most young fathers grow up in single-mother households, or they did not have a stable father figure throughout

# The role of fathers in their children's lives

their childhood (Tan & Quinlivan 2006). The lack of father figure sometimes seems to have a positive effect and young fathers in UK studies have expressed their desire to be a better father than their own fathers were (Cater & Coleman 2006, Reeves 2006, Speak *et al.* 1997). A study of young fathers with an experience of care found that they wanted to fulfil their role because their father was not there for them. The young dads perceived fatherhood as 'an opportunity to create new attachments and recreate elements of a biological family' (Tyrer *et al.* 2005: 1112) which they did not have with their own families. However, it is argued that they often find themselves ill-equipped due to the absence of guidance and role models in their lives (Tyrer *et al.* 2005). Also research in the UK has shown that father absence when growing up was given as a reason for which young men had planned to have a child (Cater & Coleman 2006). These findings echo American research based on African American young fathers, who also expressed a willingness to be involved in their children's lives based on the lack of involvement of their own fathers (Bunting & McAuley 2004).

## Case Scenario

Liam is 24 years old and has a two children, one aged three and one nine months old. He was having a casual sexual relationship with the mother when she became pregnant, and they lived far from each other. Initially, he planned to stay with his mother and visit the child and its mother weekly, as he did not want to be in a relationship with the mother. However, he soon changed his mind, and thought that since he had grown up without a father, he wanted his child to have a full-time father. He went to stay in the hostel where she lived three days a week, and eventually they got a flat together. Soon, she expressed a desire to have another child, and he liked the idea too, although he warned her that it would be hard. After the birth of the second baby, the mother developed post-natal depression and was unable to care for the children. Liam is now the full-time carer and cannot work as a result. He has however decided that he is going to look after his children and does not want to lose them. Liam is prepared to be a single father in the future, if his girlfriend does not get better and leaves.



199

## Housing:
## places and spaces where young men father

**Housing**

Providing housing is one of the most popular ways in which families offer support to teenage mothers. Indeed, particularly for younger mothers remaining in the family home is a popular initial choice (SEU 1999). However, some young mothers do not have that type of family support, and one of the concerns expressed in the Social Exclusion Unit's 1999 review on teenage pregnancy was the placement of teenage mothers aged under 18 in a lone tenancy. This was to be eradicated by providing other options, mainly 'supervised semi-independent housing with support' (SEU 1999: 10). Mediating with her family to explore the option of allowing the under-18 mother to stay in the family home was also seen as a possible resource.

The 1999 report found that teenage mothers were often housed in accommodation of a poor standard, often in areas of socio-economic need which can compound pre-existing disadvantage. Moreover, it was also found that being rehoused could lead to isolation from existing sources of support, family and peers.

Housing remains an issue of concern (SETF 2006) and increasingly local authorities and housing associations are employing 'floating support' to work with young parents. These individuals can work with young parents to ensure that they are claiming the right benefits, managing their budgeting and assist them to access childcare, help them strengthen their parenting skills, give training or employment guidance amongst others. The SETF believes that all teenage parents who do not live with their parents should have such support, as being isolated from potential sources of support adds to the risk of exclusion (SETF 2006).

For young fathers, and specifically non-resident ones, one of the barriers they face is difficulty setting up a home for their child, often having to live with their own parents or other family members. When they are placed in a neighbourhood away from their child, they may struggle to raise the money for transport to pay visits, placing another hurdle to maintaining contact. Moreover, as in the case of young mothers, this may also entail those young fathers lose their previous support networks (Speak *et al.* 1997). Thus, the residency status of the mother seems to have an impact on young fathers' commitment to raising their children. There is no data that indicates how many young fathers continue to be involved with their children when they are not cohabiting with the mother and baby (Quinton *et al.* 2002). However, one strong predictor of father un-involvement was baby's mother place of residency during pregnancy. A study concerned with the predictors of young fathers' commitment to their baby found that if the mother lived at her family home, the young father was less likely to be involved in the follow-up interviews (Quinton *et al.* 2002).

Moreover, in general, young fathers who do not reside with the baby's mother have been found to be more likely to be unemployed, suffer mental health problems and engage in crime and substance abuse than resident fathers (Fathers Direct 2007). Thus, it may not be residency per se, but rather the fact that non-resident fathers are at a greater disadvantage which influences their involvement. However, it may also be that their non-resident status may offset the aforementioned positive impact that having child can have on a young man who has previously been involved, in some ways, in criminal activities.

The scarce, yet relevant, research findings with regard to young fathers and housing indicate that it is an aspect that needs to be explored, as it seems central to establishing, developing and maintaining a healthy father-child relationship.

## The father–mother relationship

**Father–mother relationship**

Added to the contextual and background difficulties, one essential influential factor in determining young fathers' involvement in their children's lives is their relationship with the mother of the child (Speak *et al.* 1997) and, as discussed in Chapter 1, the relationship with both the maternal and the paternal grandmother (Bunting & McAuley 2004, Fagan & Bernd 2007, Reeves 2006, Speak *et al.* 1997). Generally it is known that 'the frequency with which young, unwed fathers see their children and provide financial support declines rapidly over the early years' (Gavin *et al.* 2002: 267). As a consequence, it is argued that one of the reasons for which teenage pregnancy is regarded as a problem is because it often leads to unsupported motherhood (Bonnell 2004), as research shows that the lack of involvement of fathers has detrimental effects on the child and on the resources of the mother (Quinton *et al.* 2002). Also, being involved in the child's life can have a beneficial effect on the young father (Reeves 2006). These arguments support the notion that work with young fathers is important and vital (Sheriff 2007).

---

**Good Practice Box**

**Assessing the needs of a young father**

1. Does the young man need to be helped with educational qualifications (Gavin et al. 2002)?
2. Remember greater involvement is found in young fathers when they are employed.
3. Professionals working with young fathers should focus some attention on the father-mother relationship, and help repair it when necessary.
4. Young fathers often need help with housing. Is this something you can help him find out about?

---

## Father involvement and contributions

**Father involvement**

There are different conceptualisations as to what constitutes father involvement and the roles that fathers play vary amongst different cultures. Gavin *et al.* (2002: 267) identified five aspects of father involvement that they argue are common amongst all cultures, albeit with different emphasis. These are:

- endowment: acknowledging the child as one's own
- protection: protecting the child from sources of potential danger and contributing to decisions that affect the child's welfare
- provision: ensuring that the child's material needs are met
- formation: socialisation activities, such as discipline and teaching
- care-giving: meeting the physical needs of the baby by feeding, diapering, bathing and so on.

Some of the aspects above have been covered in the course of the book, such as provision. In the next section, we will focus on one aspect of the father role that is more related to formation and care-giving: play.

## Fathers, play and leisure time

**Play and leisure time**

It is, suggested that the amount of time spent by fathers with their children has not dramatically changed since the 1960s 'but what has changed is men's use of such time to get actively involved in such things as playing with their young children, bathing, changing and putting them to bed' (Lewis & Warin 2001: 5). Although in broad terms, fathers are increasingly involved in childcare (Drape 2003), there is also the belief that the childcare role adopted by fathers is questionable, with most fathers mainly getting involved in play activities rather than actual caring ones (Brannen & Nielsen 2006, Golombok 2000). To date, there is no research that specifically tackles the issue of young fathers and play, and how they engage with their children during leisure time. However, it would be expected that the benefits that children gain from sharing play with their (older) fathers would be the same for children of young dads.

Play time, however, cannot be overstated as a positive, and particular, contribution that fathers make to their children's upbringing (Beets et al. 2007):

- The way that mothers and fathers play with their children appears to be significantly different, with fathers engaging in more physical and outdoor play (Lewis & Warin 2001, Beets et al. 2007), as well acting as planners of the activities, such as trips to the park (Davison et al. 2003).

- Mothers, on the other hand, are more likely to assist the realisation of leisure activities by, for example, paying the fees (Davison et al. 2003).

- Another significant difference is that fathers more often engage in play that is not based around objects and is more spontaneous, whereas mothers are more conversing and didactic; their play style tends to be more object based. In short, it is believed that fathers tend to excite children and mothers contain them (Paquette 2004). This may be meaningful in terms of the way children form attachments to their parents.

- It is important, however, to recognise individual differences between mothers and fathers; the father as 'play mate' and mother as 'care giver' will not always apply (Tamis Le-Monda 2004) and is not an accurate representation of all families. Particularly if we take into account the changing nature of fatherhood, the breakdown of traditional gendered roles as well as diversity of family forms, it becomes obvious that a clear cut distinction cannot be made between mothers and fathers and their roles (Bretherton *et al.* 2005). The point seems to be that physical and active play make a positive contribution to children's development. As a result, it is a way of getting involved that should be encouraged amongst fathers.

---

**Good Practice Box**

### Encouraging play

- It may be beneficial to encourage young fathers to play with their children, as a positive, and often cheap, way to interact with them.

- However, as Beets et al. (2007: 1) point out 'the effectiveness of family-based activity interventions depends on when parents have opportunities to be present for their child's activity'. Thus the professional working with young fathers should be sensitive to living arrangements, working or studying schedules of young fathers, when encouraging them to play. Since time seems to be a key theme, budgeting time during the week or weekend, to spend some playing with the children would be necessary to achieve fathers' engagement (Beets et al. 2007).

- An Australian study found that dads regarded leisure time with their children as important for the following reasons (Harrington 2006: 181):

  1. 'communicating and sharing with their children'

  2. 'guiding them and inculcating values'

  3. 'recognising that, as parents, they only have limited opportunities to spend with their children and guide their future development'.

- This study concluded that father's play time with children demonstrates the emotional connection between them.

---

## Father–child attachment: bonding and security

**Bonding and security**

The play and leisure time that fathers spend with their children may aid the father-child bond and attachment. It is observed by Roggman (2004: 228) that there is a range of theories about parenting generally and mothering in particular, but that 'studying fathers can be more challenging though, because of the current lack of a strong guiding theory about fathering. Somewhat like a traveler without a map or guidebook, a researcher observing fathers may notice interesting things without understanding clearly what they mean.'

Attachment theory, developed by John Bowlby, claims that 'the quality of nursing and care a child receives from mother in the first years after birth, is of great importance to the child's further development' (Cugmas 1998: 65) and has been a crucial approach in the study of child development and parent–child relationships. However, the aforementioned discourses of new fatherhood and the more involved roles that fathers have been expected to adopt, have meant that a number of researchers have expanded attachment theories to study fathers (Bretherton *et al.* 2005).

While attachment has been studied mainly in relation to the caring role, gendered play interactions between fathers, mothers and their children have also been related to the different ways in which children form attachments to their parents (Bretherton *et al*. 2005). For instance, over 25 years ago, in 1981, Lamb spoke of the different ways in which children form attachment to their parents: with mothers through comfort and care, with fathers through active play (Tamis Le-Monda 2004). Although it is argued that this is not as clear cut, and that fathers can form attachments to their children by also adopting caring roles (Tamis Le-Monda, 2004), it is nevertheless an important point that when fathers are seen as engaging in what may seem as meaningless rough play, it may in fact be contributing to their emotional attachment to their children (Paquette 2004).

Although Paquette's theory has been criticised for its sharp gendered division, it is acknowledged as a step beyond mother-centred transferable theories and one that suggests that some fathers may contribute in a specific and particular way to their children's development (Tamis Le-Monda 2004). However, this can be regarded as one of the ways in which fathers and their children can bond, but by no means the only one.

## Paquette's father-specific theory

Paquette (2004) proposed a father-specific theory that moves away from the mother-centred attachment theory, which is based on the idea of a parent–child bond through comforting and calming children in times of stress.

- Because this role has traditionally been ascribed to the mother, attachment theory's suitability to study father–child bonds has been questioned.

- Instead, it is believed that 'children may develop a different type of attachment with each of their parents' (Paquette 2004: 201). He suggests that the way in which fathers engage in physical and rough-and-tumble play, which he calls the father–child activation relationship, provides the father–child emotional bond, in the same way that mother's comforting and calming children in attachment theory does.

- How this happens is by fathers opening their children to the world, by playing in teasing in a physical manner, as Paquette (2004: 194) explains:

'Men seem to have a tendency to excite, surprise, and momentarily destabilize children; they also tend to encourage children to take risks, while at the same time ensuring the latter's safety and security, thus permitting children to learn to be braver in unfamiliar situations, as well as to stand up for themselves.'

Another aspect of parent–child attachment that has been explored by researchers is the characteristics of the child, which will no doubt also play a role in creating a bond (Cugmas 1998), in the same way that they contribute to the aforementioned parental stress. This, again, will have to be assessed by professionals wanting to involve fathers in their children's lives.

## The four pillars model

The diagram-model 'The four pillars of young father support' (Figure 6.3) represents four axes of father involvement in their children's lives, and they are the aspects that professionals could focus on when attempting to support young fathers or assessing the situation of young fathers in order to offer support. It draws together some of the issues discussed in the chapter.

**Figure 6.3**     **The four pillars**

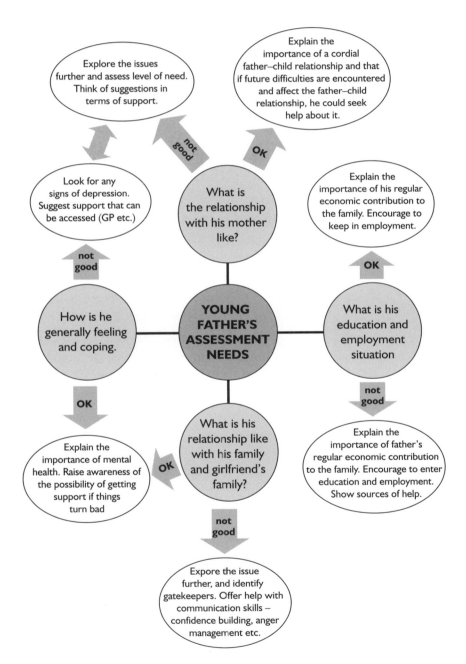

The four pillars are some of the difficulties previously discussed in the chapter: the mother–father relationship, the ability to financially provide, the relationship with her family and also coping with fatherhood. All of these aspects are potential contributors to parental stress, when they are negative, but at the same time, when they are positive, they can act as buffers to protect young fathers against stress. It could also be that there is a knock-on effect, so by solving one issue, say employment, another one, like the relationship with the mother (whether they are together or not), improves too. Focusing on these areas and trying to help resolve some of the aspects of their lives that are not working out, can help young fathers.

## Conclusions and implications for practice

In conclusion it can be stated that, young fathers face a multitude of problems, which have been explored in the course of the chapter, which make their relationship with their child or children more difficult to establish and maintain.Discourse theory can help professionals be reflexive about their (pre)conceived ideas about young fathers, and their roles and capabilities. It may be essential to acknowledge the way in which stereotypical negative images of young fatherhood may impact on the day-to-day treatment of young fathers by services providers.

While personal relationships, both with the mother of the child as well as with his own family and the mother's mother, affect their fathering role, young fathers often have little employment prospects which may make it difficult to be the providers. On the other hand, it is argued that their lack of stable employment offers young fathers the flexibility to be involved in a more caring way. Popular, often negative, images of young fatherhood exist, which may help reinforce views of young fathers as useless or uninterested, which in turn may discourage them from being involved fathers and make it difficult to embrace the principles of new fatherhood. Lack of encouragement from those around them may undermine their potential to make a positive contribution or to get the necessary help.

It would seem to be important to focus on young fathers' willingness to participate in their children's lives and encourage them to fulfil their desires; to look at their potential and build on their strengths, rather than focus on their weaknesses (Stein 1997). However, one of the main difficulties for working with young fathers is that there is a 'lack of a coherent theoretical framework that provides a bridge from theories about fatherhood to the reality of practice with men and their children' (Taylor & Daniel 2000: 12). It was the aim of this chapter to help fill the gaps and bridge theory and practice.

## Young fathers and their children: key messages from research

- The breadwinner role cannot be seen as the only role that fathers assume in the family (Brannen & Nielsen 2006).
- Fathers are increasingly involved with their children, and play a more caring role than in the past (Lewis & Warin 2001).
- It is vital to acknowledge the different family types and living arrangements when thinking about the role of fathers (Marsiglio *et al.* 2000).
- Young fathers are faced with a combination of problems, which mainly relate to their background (Quinton *et al.* 2002).
- Young fathers are at a greater risk of suffering parenting stress, having adverse consequences for their relationship with their children. (Fagan & Bernd 2007)
- Young fathers are willing to be involved in their children's lives, contradicting popular negative images (Reeves 2006, Speak *et al.* 1997).
- The breadwinner role may be a difficult one for young fathers to adopt due to their lack of social and economic resources (Sigle-Rushton 2005).
- Young fathers' unemployed status may mean they enjoy greater flexibility, giving them the chance to care for their children (Tyrer *et al.* 2005).
- There is little support and encouragement from professionals and services for young fathers to play a role in their children's lives (Quinton *et al.* 2002, Tyrer *et al.* 2005, Speak *et al.* 1997).

# References

Allen, I. & Dowling, S. (1998). *Teenage Mothers: Decisions and Outcomes*. London: Policy Studies Institute.

Barclay, L. & Lupton, D. (1999). 'The experience of new fatherhood: a socio cultural analysis' in *Journal of Advanced Nursing* 29(4): 1013–1020.

Beets, M.W., Vogel, R., Chapman, S., Pitetti, K.H. & Cardinal, B.J. (2007) 'Parent's social support for children's outdoor physical activity: Do weekdays and weekends matter?' in *Sex Roles* 56: 125–131.

Belsky, J. (1984). 'The determinants of parenting: A process model' in *Child Development* 55, 83–96.

Bonnell, C. (2004). 'Why is teenage pregnancy conceptualized as a social problem?' in *Culture, Health & Sexuality* 6(3): 255–272.

Brannen, J. & Nielsen, A. (2006). 'From fatherhood to fathering: Transmission and change among British fathers in four-generation families' in *Sociology* 40(2): 335–352.

Bretherton, I., Lambert, J.D. & Golby, B. (2005). 'Involved fathers of preschool children as seen by themselves and their wives: Accounts of attachment, socialization, and companionship' in *Attachment & Human Development* 7(3): 229–251.

Bunting, L. & McAuley, C. (2004). 'Research review: Teenage pregnancy and parenthood: the role of fathers' in *Child and Family Social Work* 9: 295–303.

Carabine, J. (2001). 'Unmarried motherhood 1830–1990: A genealogical analysis' in Whetherell, M., Taylor, S. & Yates, S.J. (eds) *Discourses as Data: A Guide for Analysis*. London: Sage Publications: 267–310.

Cater, S. & Coleman, L. (2006). *'Planned' Teenage Pregnancy: Perspectives of Young Parents from Disadvantaged Backgrounds*. Bristol: Policy Press.

Coin de Carvalho, J.E. (2007). '"How can a child be a mother?" Discourse on teenage pregnancy in a Brazilian favela' in Culture, *Health and Sexuality* 9(2): 109–120.

Cugmas, Z. (1998). 'The correlation between children's personal behavioural characteristics and indicators of children's attachment to their mother or father, respectively' in *Early Child Development and Care* 143: 65–78.

Davison, K.K., Cutting, T.M. & Birch, L.L. (2003). 'Parents' activity-related parenting practices predict girls' physical activity' in *Medicine and Science in Sports and Exercise* 35(9): 1589–1595.

Department for Children, Schools and Families (2007). *Teenage parents next steps: guidance for local authorities and primary care trusts*. Nottingham: DCSF Publications.

Department of Education and Skills (2006). *Teenage Pregnancy Next Steps: Guidance for Local Authorities and Primary Care Trusts on Effective Delivery of Local Strategies*. London: HMSO.

Drape, J. (2003). 'Men's passage to fatherhood: an analysis of the contemporary relevance of transition theory' in *Nursing Inquiry* 10(1): 66–78.

Duncan, S. (2007). 'What's the problem with teenage pregnancy? And what's the problem with teenage policy?' in *Critical Social Policy* 27: 307.

Edin, K. & Kefalas, M. (2005). *Promises I can keep. Why Poor Women put Motherhood before Marriage*. Berkeley: University of California Press.

Ermisch, J. & Francesconi, M. (2000). 'Patterns of household and family formation' in Berthoud, R. & Gershuny, J. (eds), *Seven Years in the Lives of British Families: Evidence on the Dynamics of Social Change from the British Household Panel Survey*. Bristol: The Policy Press.

Fagan, J. & Bernd, E. (2007). 'Adolescent fathers' parenting stress, social support, and involvement with infants' in *Journal of Research on Adolescence* 17(1): 1–22.

Fathers Direct (2007). *Young fathers: Influences, Barriers, Possibilities* (available online at: www.fatherhoodinstitute.org/index.php?id = 13&cID = 575).

Featherstone, B. (2003). 'Taking fathers seriously' in *British Journal of Social Work* 33: 239–254.

Gavin, L.E., Black, M.M., Minor, S., Abel, Y., Papas, M.S. & Bentley, M.E. (2002). 'Young, disadvantaged fathers' involvement with their infants: an ecological perspective' in *Journal of Adolescent Mental Health* 31(3): 266–276.

Golombok, S. (2000). *Parenting. What really counts?* London: Routledge.

Hacking, I. (1998). 'The archaeology of Foucault' in Hoy, D.C. (ed.) *Foucault: A Critical Reader*. Oxford: Blackwell.

Hall, S. (2001). 'Foucault: Power, Knowledge and Discourse' in Whetherell, M., Taylor, S. & Yates, S.J. (eds) *Discourses as Data: A Guide for Analysis*. London: Sage Publications: 72–81.

Harrington, M. (2006). 'Sport and leisure as contexts for fathering in Australian families' in *Leisure Studies* 25(2): 165–183.

Henwood, K. & Procter, J. (2003). 'The "good father": Reading men's accounts of paternal involvement during the transition to first-time fatherhood' in *British Journal of Social Psychology* 42: 337–335.

Higginbottom, G.M.A., Mathers, N., Marsh, P., Kirkham, M., Owen, J.M. & Serrant-Green, L. (2006) 'Young people of minority ethnic origin in England and early parenthood: Views from young parents and service providers' in *Social Science and Medicine* 63: 858–870.

Hudson, F. & Ineichen, B. (1991). *Taking it Lying Down: Sexuality and Teenage Motherhood*. Basingstoke: MacMillan Publishing.

Jones, G. (2003). *The Youth Divide: Diverging Paths to Adulthood*. York: Joseph Rowntree Foundation.

Lewis, J. (2001). 'Debate and issues regarding marriage and cohabitation in the British and American literature' in *International Journal of Law, Policy and the Family* 15: 159–184.

Lewis, C. & Warin, J. (2001). 'What Good Are Dads?' in *Father Facts* 1(1). www.fathersdirect.com.

Lewis, C., Papacost, A. & Warin, J. (2002). *Cohabitation, Separation and Fatherhood*. York: Joseph Rowntree Foundation, YPS.

Marsiglio, W., Amato, P., Randal, D.D. & Lamb, M.E. (2000). 'Scholarship on fatherhood in the 1990s and beyond' in *Journal of Marriage and the Family* 62: 1173–1191.

Matta, D.S. & Knudson-Martin, C. (2006). 'Father responsivity: Couple processes and the coconstruction of fatherhood' in *Family Process* 45(1): 19–37.

McBride, B., Schoppe, S.J. & Rane, T.R. (2002). 'Child characteristics, parenting stress, and parental involvement: Fathers versus mothers' in *Journal of Marriage and Family* 64: 998–1011.

Murray, C. (1996). *Charles Murray and the Underclass. The Developing Debate.* IEA Health and Welfare Unit with the Sunday Times.

Nayak, A. (2006). 'Displaced masculinities: Chavs, youth and class in the post-industrial city' in *Sociology* 40(5): 813–831.

Office for National Statistics (2002). *Labour Force Survey.* London: The Stationery Office.

Office for National Statistics (2005). *Birth statistics: Review of the Registrar General on Births and Patterns of Family Building in England and Wales, 2004.* Series FM1, no 33. London: The Stationery Office.

Office for National Statistics (2007). *Social Trends 37.* London: The Stationery Office.

Paquette, D. (2004). 'Theorizing the father-child relationship: Mechanisms and developmental outcomes' in *Human Development* 47: 193–219.

Pears, K.C., Pierce, S.L., Kim, H.K., Capaldi, D.M. & Owen, L.D. (2005). 'The timing of entry into fatherhood in young, at-risk men' in *Journal of Marriage and the Family* 67: 429–447.

Phillips, N. & Hardy, C. (2002). *Discourse Analysis. Investigating Processes of Social Construction.* London: Sage.

Quinton, D., Pollock, S. & Golding, J. (2002). *The Transition to Fatherhood in Young Men: Influences on Commitment. A report to the ESRC.* University of Bristol.

Quinlivan, J. & Condon, J. (2005). 'Anxiety and depression in fathers in teenage pregnancy' in *Australian and New Zealand Journal of Psychiatry* 39: 915–920.

Reeves, J. (2003). *They Should Still Be Out Playing: A Contemporary Analysis of Young Pregnant Women/Mothers in the Care System.* Unpublished Thesis for Master of Philosophy in Social Work. University of Kent, Canterbury.

Reeves, J. (2006). ' "Steppin' up to the plate". Exploring the stories young, disadvantaged fathers in the UK and USA tell about the transition to fatherhood', paper presented at the International Sociological Association, South Africa 2006.

Roggman, L. (2004). 'Do fathers just want to have fun? Commentary on theorizing the father-child relationship' in *Human Development* 47: 228–236.

Rowlingson, K. & McKay, S. (2005). 'Lone motherhood and socioeconomic disadvantage: insights from quantitative and qualitative evidence' in *The Sociological Review* 53: 30–49.

Sigle-Rushton, W. (2005). 'Young fatherhood and subsequent disadvantage in the United Kingdom' in *Journal of Marriage and the Family* 67: 735–753.

Simms, M. & Smith, C. (1986). *Teenage Mothers and their Partners.* London: HMSO.

Sheriff, N. (2007). *Supporting Young Fathers: Examples of Promising Practice.*

Brighton: Trust for the Study of Adolescence.

Smith, A., Morton, S. & Wasoff, F. (2007). *Working Fathers in Europe, Earning and Caring?* CRFR research briefing 30. Edinburgh: Centre for Research on Families and Relationships.

Social Exclusion Unit (1999). *Teenage Pregnancy*. London: HMSO.

Social Exclusion Unit (2005). *Transitions: Young Adults with Complex Needs.* London: HMSO.

Social Exclusion Task Force (2006). *Reaching Out: Progress on Social Exclusion.* London: HMSO.

Speak, S., Cameron, S. & Gilroy, R. (1997). *Young Single Fathers: Participation in Fatherhood – Bridges and Barriers.* Oxford: Family Policy Studies Centre.

Stein, M. (1997). *What Works in Leaving Care?* Summary. Essex: Barnardo's.

Swann, C., Bowe, K., McCormick, G. & Kosmin, M. (2003). *Teenage Pregnancy and Parenthood: A Review of Reviews.* London: Health Development Agency.

Tabberer, S., Hall, C., Prendergast, S. & Webster, A. (2000). *Teenage Pregnancy and Choice.* York: Joseph Rowntree Foundation.

Tamis Le-Monda, C. (2004). 'Conceptualizing fathers' roles: Playmates and more' in *Human Development* 47: 220–227.

Tan, L.H. & Quinlivan, J.A. (2006). 'Domestic violence, single parenthood, and fathers in the setting of teenage pregnancy' in *Journal of Adolescent Health* 38: 201–207.

Taylor, J. & Daniel, B. (2000). 'The rhetoric vs. the reality in child care and protection: ideology and practice in working with fathers' in *Journal of Advanced Nursing* 31(1): 12–19.

Tyrer, P., Chase, E., Warwick, I. & Aggleton, P. (2005). ' "Dealing with it": Experiences of young fathers in and leaving care' in *British Journal of Social Work* 35: 1107–1121.

Wellings, K., Nanchahal, K., MacDowell, W., McManus, S. & Erens, R. (2001). 'Sexual health in Britain: Early heterosexual experiences' in *Lancet* 358: 1843–1850.

# Chapter 7
# Recklessness, rescue and responsibility:
## Jane Reeves

*Fatherhood as a factor of desistence amongst young men involved within the criminal justice system*

## Introduction

> 'I've been to court probably more times than the judges have'. (Luke, young father aged 15, in Reeves 2006)

As this book has pointed out, young fathers are on the cusp of several different types of change. Firstly, they are making the transition to fatherhood and secondly, they are moving from adolescence to adulthood with all of the inherent complexities of contemporary masculinities. Thirdly, young men also have to negotiate the complexities of family life, relationships and pressures to conform with their peers as well as negotiating and sustaining intimate sexual relationships. Fourthly, many young men who become fathers are also involved in youth crime during their teenage years, often with their friends, thus placing further pressure on their lives.

The purpose of this chapter is to focus on the common features and links between young fatherhood and youth offending, as many health and social care practitioners are involved with young people who are on the fringes of criminality and anti-social behaviour; indeed, some programmes aimed at young fathers use young men who are incarcerated due to their position as being a 'captive audience'. Youth crime is currently an issue with a high profile in contemporary society, particularly around the 'hoodie' subculture and 'respect' policy agenda of the end of the Blair era in 2006 (Henderson *et al.* 2007). The chapter will initially examine the nature and features of youth crime, with particular reference to young men. It will then argue that young fatherhood is often a factor in youth crime, with both issues sharing similar underlying causes, but that ultimately, and ironically, teenage pregnancy can provide a solution for some young men to a life of crime. This chapter draws heavily on the evidence gained from the study by Reeves (2006).

## Recklessness, risk and youth crime

**Risk and youth crime**

Coleman and Hendry (2004) suggest that the concept of risk taking in adolescence is 'ill defined' (2004: 1221) yet can focus around 'thrill seeking', 'controlled risk taking' and 'irresponsibility' (2004: 121). Connell (1995) argues that risk taking behaviours during the teenage years, particularly being aggressive, 'tough' and 'hard', appear to be components of an image of contemporary hegemonic masculinity. Frosh *et al.* (2002) point out that for some young men adolescence is a time of 'hedonistic self indulgence and lack of control' (2002: 30). Connell (2000) refers to this phase in a young man's life as the 'classic wild oats sowing script' (2000: 98) and Coleman and Hendry (2004) argue that this type of activity is engaged in, in order to look 'cool or grown up' (2004: 128). Connell, however, states that this type of risky behaviour is undertaken 'in order to be masculine' (2000: 185). Connell explains that the peer group 'sustains' a version of masculinity at a particular point in a young man's life and this group membership offers a validation of masculine status.

## Making the transition to adulthood

**Transition to adulthood**

The transition period from childhood to adulthood is now generally considered to be a heterogeneous experience (Jones 2003, Raffo & Reeves 2000, Thomson *et al.* 2002). Reasons suggested for these changes and the variety of transition experiences include the diversification of educational experience and alterations to the youth labour market, resulting in the limitation of employment opportunities for some young people (Jones 2003). Jones argues that a consequence of these changes has been to encourage some groups of teenagers to stay on in education. However, she also argues that the outcomes for young men who do not stay on at school, go on to further or higher education or get a job are that they are increasingly unable to access routes to independence and consequently crime is more likely to play a part in their lives.

There is also wide agreement in recent research regarding the way in which some constructions of young masculinity have been problematised, indicating a crisis for some young men (Frosh *et al.* 2002, McDowell 2001). A great deal of the concern focuses on a perceived increase in:

- anti-social behaviour

- delinquency (Stephen & Squires 2003)

- sexual abuse perpetration (Frosh *et al.* 2002)

- poor educational attainment (McDowell 2001)

- suicide rates for young men (Lloyd & Forrest 2001, McDowell 2001); indeed, as McQueen and Henwood (2002) highlight, suicide is the second most common cause of death in males aged 15 to 34 in the UK.

Set against these factors and further contributing to a problematised discourse are media induced 'moral panics' regarding male gang culture and violence (Welch *et al.* 2002), joy riding (Stephen & Squires 2003) and latterly a binge-drinking culture.

Lloyd and Forrest (2001) argue that there is 'plenty of evidence to suggest that young men exhibit more risk behaviours and take more risks than young women' (2001: 44). Not all commentary on risk-taking is negative. Lloyd and Forrest (2001) argue that taking risks is a means to developing self-awareness, self-confidence and self-reliance. Generally, however, studies tend to indicate increasing involvement of young working class men in risk-taking behaviours.

- For example, working class young men tend to smoke 50% more cigarettes than those from middle class groups and this pattern is repeated for drinking, with working-class young men drinking more and earlier than other groups and than young women (Lloyd & Forrest 2001). As Dennison and Coleman report 'drinking alcohol is most closely associated with young men' (2000: 23).

- In addition, early sexual activity is also associated with working-class status (Wellings *et al.* 1994) and particularly with young men without qualifications who do not live with their parents at the age of 16 (Wellings *et al.* 2001). Although reliability can be an issue in this type of data, young men from working-class backgrounds are cited as, on average, having sexual intercourse two years prior to middle-class young men (Wellings *et al.* 1994).

- Moreover, although young people are reputedly using contraceptives more frequently than in the past (Wellings & Mitchell 1998), age and gender seem to be significant influences on this. A young, working-class male is less likely to mention having used contraceptives than a working-class young woman, although both boys and girls are vulnerable to not using contraceptives during the early stages of a relationship (Dennison & Coleman 2000, Wellings *et al.* 1994). Explanations for young men's reluctance to use contraceptives vary and include them reporting a reduction in the perception of sexual pleasure through condom use (Thomson & Holland 1998), as well as the negotiation of intricate power relations between young men and young women during sexual activity (Frost 2001).

In their Review of Reviews on teenage pregnancy in the UK Swann *et al.* (2003) remark that, as with young mothers, there is a link between being a young father and being exposed to deprivation and exclusion. Young fathers are more likely to come from lower socio-economic groups (Hudson & Ineichen 1991, Swann *et al.* 2003) and families facing financial hardships (Kiernan 1995, Tyrer *et al.* 2005). In addition these young men are likely to have left school at the minimum age. Furthermore, as Tyrer *et al.* (2005: 1108) remark, 'Teenage fathers are more likely to have engaged in youth offending, with some estimates suggesting that more than a quarter of young men in young offenders institutions are already fathers or expectant fathers.' Youth offending and engagement in anti-social behaviour is therefore a key feature of the debate on young fatherhood and both issues are, arguably, highly politicised issues.

## Young fathers and youth offending

**Youth offending**

Evidence on youth offending (Whyte 2004, Unruh *et al.* 2003) suggests that paths into criminal activity are associated with early involvement and multiple disadvantages. As Whyte highlights there is a complex relationship between individual features and social contexts which are associated with youth crime. These include individual characteristics, school and community factors. These have been summarised in Table 7.1. (For other references see Webster *et al.* (2006); Laub & Sampson (2003).)

**Table 7.1**

### Features associated with youth crime

Adapted from Whyte 2004 and Unruh *et al.* 2003.

| Individual characteristics | Family features | Factors from the school environment | Community factors |
|---|---|---|---|
| Impulsivity, personal controls | Parenting style – inconsistent, harsh | Truancy | Drug and alcohol availability |
| Anti-social attitudes | Poor parental supervision | Poor achievement | Poor local amenities |
| Binge drinking | | Disaffection | |
| Drug use | Unstable family structure | Aggressive behaviour | High crime rates |
| Involvement in crime before | Criminality in the family | Failing school | High rates of social exclusion and disadvantage |
| Contact with delinquent peers | | Gang membership | |

As this table indicates there are often combinations of macro and micro ingredients which coexist to produce the outcome of youth crime. As Whyte (2004) summarises, understanding the interaction of these aspects is a key feature for practitioners who work with young offenders:

Those concerned to reduce offending among children and young people, in addition to understanding the developmental needs and social circumstances of the young people, must also develop an understanding of the nature of crime as a social phenomenon; the significance of its form... the social and moral context.... the nature and shape of crime [and] its direction through time and space. (2004: 8)

Lack of parental supervision (or lack of engagement with parental figures) combined with a powerful peer presence in an environment where alcohol and drugs are 'de rigueur' often result in criminal activity. Graham and Bowling (1995) highlight that there are three risk factors which explain the continuation of offending. These include:

- a high frequency of previous offending
- continued contact with delinquent friends
- continued heavy drinking and drug use.

## Case transcript

**Peter, a young father, explains that stealing became a method to fund his drug habit:**

*Peter:* ...the cars were just taking them for a bit of fun.

*Jane:* Why?

*Peter:* Because there were plenty of fields around where we was. We used to take them in the woods and smash them up and things. Then as I got older we started realising that we needed money to buy the drugs and there was money in taking the cars.

Webster *et al.* (2006) also highlight how one young man, Micky, was 'struggling' to escape from the influence of people he once considered friends in his quest to desist from drug use:

*I am trying to keep myself to myself 'cos, like, now you find a best mate and he'll sit there and tell you he's clean then two minutes later, it'll be 'jaway, let's go get some f*****g gear' (heroin) and I'm like 'I don't even wanna talk to you'. (2006: 13)*

Analogous with youth crime, the path into young fatherhood is associated with a complex, yet similar, interaction of factors – represented in Table 7.2.

**Table 7.2**  **Features associated with young fatherhood**

| Individual characteristics | Family features | Factors from the school environment | Community factors |
|---|---|---|---|
| Early sexual experiences<br><br>Lack of contraceptive use<br><br>Peer pressure<br><br>Masculinity<br><br>Involvement in crime | Single parent/ parent with multiple relationships<br><br>Raised by someone other than biological parent<br><br>Low socio-economic status<br><br>Parent with alcoholism<br><br>Lack of father figure/role model | Truancy<br><br>Lack of sex education | Availability of contraceptives<br><br>High rates of social exclusion and disadvantage<br><br>High rates of crime |

It can be seen that there are many overlapping features in Tables 7.1 and 7.2, within the psychosocial terrain of individual and family relationships and also of wider community features, linking youth crime and young fatherhood. Firstly, as the example above indicates, peer pressure has been indicated as both a feature of youth offending and young fatherhood.

## Case transcripts

As Will, 19, a young father from the US from Reeves, (2006) study describes, part of his journey towards responsibility since becoming a father has been facing up to the limitations of his friendships or his 'homies':

You think your friends is always going to be there for you and everything and I go 'yeah whatever'. I moved out, where were my friends? I am

> in trouble with the police, where were my friends? They're not there.
>
> **Similarly Raleem, 24, points out the transitory nature of the relationship you have with friends and emphasises how difficult it can be to find support from them when you have a child:**
>
> You can't always rely on friends because I was popular with them when I was getting girls and I was on the football team, but when your luck runs out and you become a burden to them they don't always want to be your friend.

Secondly, absence from school is also a risk factor for both social problems – figures for truancy suggest that it is more often a problem for young men, with a clear link established between frequent offenders and 'hanging around' street corners with other truants (Webster *et al.* 2006). Truanting also removes young people from PHSE lessons where relationships, sexual behaviour and responsibilities may be covered. Thirdly, the issue of parenting is also a characteristic of both issues, particularly in relation to fathering. In addition, young people who are not brought up by a biological parent may be particularly vulnerable. Fourthly, living and being brought up in conditions where social exclusion dominate the environment and community resources has also been shown to be a clear factor affecting both social issues (SEU 1999, 2004).

## Desistence theories and 'critical moments'

**Desistence theories**

Recent research has given some insights into the factors, processes and interventions by which individuals desist from crime and underpinning these factors are three theoretical approaches: maturation reform theory, social bonds theory and narrative theory (Maruna 2000). Maturation reform theory relates desistence from crime to age and the developmental 'growing up' process; social bonds theory emphasises the importance of family ties and the importance of education and employment opportunity, and narrative theories emphasise the importance of an individual's emerging and changing sense of identity and self which recognise links with others. Burnett (2000) noted that those who were the most successful in desisting from crime were those who were the most confident in doing this; re-positioning and reforming their sense of identity and image. Maruna (2000) points out that key to this process is the belief that the individual has begun to take control of his life and that he has a positive plan that he can influence and work with. This model is illustrated in terms of some of the data discussed below, where there is a clear association between the life transition from adolescence to parenthood and the adoption of a new, non-criminalised identity.

## The importance of critical moments

**Critical moments**

The focus on 'critical moments' (Henderson *et al.* 2007) in the lives of young people follows other commentators who have drawn attention to the importance of particular moments in the biographies of young people; for example Denzin (1989) talks of 'epiphanies' and others describe 'turning points' (Mandlebaum 1973) whilst Giddens (1991) frames them in terms of 'fateful moments'.

The distinction between the above concepts and critical moments is that the latter are only recognised as significant with hindsight. Critical moments can variously include family situations and relationships such as divorce, moving house or location, or rights of passage such as the impact of 'coming out'. Of significance here is the reflection that some young men go through about the importance of a relationship and the birth of their child.

As Henderson *et al.* (2007) point out, it is clear that some critical moments are more consequential than others and they can have longer-term consequences. It is not possible to assess the long-term impact that the significant moment of becoming a teenage father has on a young man, as there is a dearth of longitudinal studies on this area, however the shorter-term impact is evident from the comments detailed below.

**Good Practice Box**

**Recognising critical moments**

Is it possible to do a life story book with a young man to identify any particular critical moments or turning points in his life?

What led up to the critical moment?

How did the young person handle the situation?

Were there individuals who helped the young man and what role did they play?

What were the positive and negative features of the experience?

## Rescue:
## swapping a criminal career for a family one

**Rescue**

Recklessness during adolescence is not a new theme in social research. Indeed, involvement in deviant behaviour is often described as a feature of working-class youth.

However, what has emerged from the research of Reeves 2006 as a significant finding is that for some young men who become fathers there are two further, more optimistic, phases in their lives to which the pregnancy, birth of the child and subsequent social relationships contribute. Specifically, the overall narratives of the young men demonstrate how some position their partners, or the birth of their child as effecting a distinct change in their identities: critical people in encouraging desistence.

In the following case examples we see the young men identify features which are described as significant in contributing to them being rescued from their previous reckless and anti-social identities:

1. Some participants present their partner as being 'different' from other young women they have had relationships with.

2. Connected to this, their current partner is described as significant by saving them from their previous reckless behaviour.

3. Some young men present themselves as sacrificing this previous anti-social behaviour for their partner and/or baby.

# Recklessness, rescue and responsibility

In the example below Luke describes the sacrifice he has made in keeping out of trouble ('that' in line one) for several months, since he has been with his current girlfriend who is pregnant with his baby. He also explains that she is 'different' from previous girlfriends:

## Case transcript

*Luke:* I don't do that, I ain't done that in like seven months now because I've been with my girlfriend for ages and I ain't done that with her. Like I ain't done nothing wrong when I was with her, I kept out of trouble for like seven months.

*Interviewer:* Have you had lots of other girlfriends?

*Luke:* Yeah she's proper different.

Interviewer: What's different about her?

*Luke:* Because she's like come from sort of like posh, not posh but like a posh family, you know like a perfect family and all that.

Interviewer: What's a perfect family?

*Luke:* Don't do nothing wrong, who thinks crime is bad and all like stuff like that and she's like doing good at school and she's in like the higher sets, everyone thinks she's a boffin and all that.

I was doing — I was literally getting nicked every day or every two days and all that. I just wanted to stop because I was with her and she didn't like it.

*Interviewer:* What did she say to you?

*Luke:* Like she said she didn't want me to do it no more and all that, so I didn't.

Staying in and distancing themselves from their previous lives and contacts is a theme echoed by other young men. Daniel and Dwayne, like Luke, emphasise how 'different' their current partners are and how these young women have changed them:

## Case transcripts

*Daniel:* She was just quiet and she brought me down a peg or two.

*Interviewer:* How do you mean?

*Daniel:* Well up until then I was always getting into trouble but since I met her I ain't got into trouble.

**Similarly, Dwayne explains:**

*Dwayne:* I don't know, most of the other girls I used to go out with and that, they used to be 'little divs' and that, but she's calmed me down a lot and that.

*Interviewer:* What do you men by 'little divs'? What does that mean?

*Dwayne:* Don't know. They always like to cause arguments with boys and that who walked past with like me and my mates and that, always used to frighten them. But like since I've been with my girlfriend now, she's kept me out of trouble, well for a little while to be honest.

*Interviewer:* How does she do that?

*Dwayne:* Don't know, I just stay in, I don't go out anymore.

I just stay in with her most of the time.

## Young women as agents of change

**Agents of change**

Like Dwayne, Luke and Daniel, John also presents his girlfriend as an agent of change. He sees her as a facilitator moving him from a delinquent phase of his life to one where he is not dependent upon drugs: 'my girlfriend. She like helped me through my addiction saying look "calm it down". She didn't stop me just like that but she was saying "listen do this much and then do this much and then do this much."'

'Calm' is a word that both John and Dwayne use when describing their partners' influence on them and their behaviour. Like John, Peter explains how his partner encouraged him to rescue himself from his drug addiction. I ask how he gave up taking drugs: ' Kelly. She told me it was killing me basically. The thoughts were in my mind already and she just boosted the thoughts I was having and I decided enough was enough. Luckily enough I think I stopped taking them easy compared to a lot of people. But I suppose I had the support to do it.'

Peter describes how in Kelly he found someone he was prepared to listen to about his drug taking. Peter describes himself as being ready to give up drugs but needed motivation: 'she's the motivation behind me, she kicks my backside and says "get on with it"'. In their research on young people in transition Johnston *et al.* (2000: 3) remark that 'individuals' movements into and out of drug use and criminal activity were complex, varied and often dependent upon other experiences'. They found influential factors in preventing involvement included the formation of new personal relationships.

## Becoming more responsible? Being a provider

**Being a provider**

> She said she was pregnant and I thought, I want that. (Victor, age 16)

At the time of his interview Victor was 16 and still at school waiting to sit his GCSE examinations, an event not usually associated with being a young father. He clearly has a vision of himself as a provider for both his partner and his baby:

### Case transcript

*Victor:* I'm going to go, when I leave, well I'm going to get a job [...] fitting windows for a little while because I know how to do it and it's quite good money in it, if you know what you do. Do that till the baby's born just so I've a little bit of money, and then when we settle down and got our own place somewhere, then I'll go and get an apprenticeship as electrician, plumber or do a bit of building.

Victor and Luke are both fathers in waiting and locate themselves as wanting to provide for their new families. At the moment Victor is prevented from doing this as he is still at school, although currently on exam leave. Luke, although a year younger than Victor, has a job with his father, due to him being permanently excluded from school. This is an unusual position and is perhaps indicative of Luke's dislike and negative experiences of school and the failures within the education system in providing for him.

## Talking about responsibility

**Talking about responsibility**

The issue of responsibility was directly talked about in two main ways:

- firstly, the sense of regret at wasting the teenage years
- secondly, by being confronted in their own communities with similar anti-social behaviour they described engaging in, forcing them into the role of a protector to their young families.

Daniel expresses his regret at wasting money: 'Now I realise that all the money I've wasted when I've been working [...] drinking, like when I've been going out with my mates having a drink, I should have saved it for a rainy day really.' For Daniel, like Victor and Luke, the priority of space for his new family to be together is pressing, as he is currently living with his father whilst his partner and baby are living with her parents.

Quieniart (2004) argues that the desire for and achievement of personal space marks a definitive transition to the adult world for young fathers and a signal to the outside world that this is a new family and they are at the head of it. Being separated, particularly with the mother and baby living elsewhere, causes tensions, allows the interference of others in the relationship and inhibits the exercise of responsibility. Daniel describes feeling like this below:

## Case transcript

### The importance of space

Daniel: I was seeing it (the baby) every day but then there was an argument on the house and her dad started going off his head and that and he said to me that you're not allowed in the house no more, so then that obviously caused me and Sally to have an argument, we split up, well we didn't split up, we was having a break. I was picking Paige up every Saturday and looking after her and then I went and then we got back together and now she comes down here every weekend.

# Recklessness, rescue and responsibility

## A moral dilemma

Taking up a position of responsibility is also described by some of the young men as adopting a protective identity towards their new family unit. As Manuel explains he has had to assume a reliable and dependable identity and be available to his wife and children, a totally different identity from driving stolen cars recklessly at 80 mph. He claims this reliable identity is difficult to maintain as, ironically for him, his family home regularly comes under 'bombardment' from local youths who throw stones and verbal abuse at him and his family.

### Case transcript

*Manuel:* We get a load of youths outside, throwing stones at your windows, whacking doors and the children get really scared, saying 'come and get us, come and get us'.

*Interviewer:* How do you deal with that?

*Manuel:* I don't really know. I have been outside and had a couple of goes at the kids. Not physical, but just shouting out of the windows and that tends to make the problem worse. Erm we have phoned the police and the council.

*Interviewer:* How do you deal with the kids though? How do you deal with their worry? What do you say to them?

*Manuel:* Normally we sit there and try to reassure them that no one is going to hurt them and no one is going to get them. But, as I say, I find it really difficult because I have always said to myself that I will always make sure the kids are secure. But they are not. For me it is a very difficult life trying to explain to your children that no one is going to hurt them, it is very, very [ . . . ] what is the word? [ . . . ] very, very hard. It is not something that is easy to explain to a child of 2 or 3.

*Interviewer:* OK. So you told me that you used to race around the streets and maybe do a bit of that behaviour yourself.

*Manuel:* I did do some of that but I was never as bad as they are now. I wouldn't have deliberately thrown stones at people's windows or things like that. I wouldn't harm anyone. The kids now don't seem to care who they upset or what they upset.

# Inter-professional approaches to young fathers

Above we see Manuel experiencing an ideological dilemma (Billig *et al.* 1988) whereby two discourses, youth and 'recklessness' to which he used to belong, and that of fatherhood and 'responsibility', have collided. We, however, see him distancing himself from these past actions and adopting an adult discourse on the 'youth of today' being worse than in his day, in order to excuse his past behaviours and reconcile his two contradictory identities. He is being 'hailed' by a discourse of adult responsibility and his attachment to, or position within, the discourse of 'recklessness' has gone.

Peter outlines a similar dilemma to that of Manuel. He tells how 'every night' there is trouble from 'little buggers' who vandalise his car or smash up other people's houses. I ask Peter if he can see any similarities between how the young people are behaving and what he did in the past. Peter, like Manuel, adopts a stance associated with adult status, reflecting on how his own past behaviour was not as bad as that of young people today and exploring the different moral codes on offer.

> *Peter:* Erm. When I was younger I had different morals if you like. It's like these little buggers up here, they don't care if there is a baby seat in the car and things like that, they will still take the car and that. Believe it or not, that is things I wouldn't do, if there was a baby seat in there I wouldn't touch it. Silly little things like that.

Peter draws on a Robin Hood ethic to justify his previous position, that he only stole from the rich but the young 'buggers' of today are breaking a moral code by stealing from poorer people in his neighbourhood. His stance above is also directly related to children whereby he explains that stealing a car with a child seat in it is presented as being further down a moral chain than stealing a car without one. Arguably, he is acknowledging his past reckless identity but positioning himself as a rogue with a moral code; a person who could always be trusted with small children thus linking up his old and new identities.

The findings outlined here regarding the importance young fathers placed on the relationships with their partner and child have similarities with the conclusions of work by Laub and Sampson (2003) in the US. Their work, which features older men reflecting back on their lives, uses a life history approach encouraging the men to frame and describe the events which had taken place in their lives. Laub and Sampson emphasise the importance that the men in their study placed on the role of family, in particular meeting their wives, forming new attachments and making new social networks. Laub and Sampson argue that forming a partnership which leads to marriage was 'implicated as a predictor of desistence from crime amongst men' (Laub & Sampson 2003: 43) as was having children. Both these factors were significant in encouraging the men away from past criminal peer groups and activities.

## Repositioning: some tensions between the transition to adulthood and being a young father

**Repositioning**

Becoming a parent at any age is arguably a life-changing event or series of events (Oakely 1979). Moving from being an individual or couple to the inclusion of another dependent being is associated with physical and mental changes and challenges. As previously pointed out, the pregnancy and the birth of a child in the early to mid-teenage years is problematised and is generally regarded as having poor consequences for both parent and child (Hudson & Ineichen 1991, SEU 1999, Swann *et al.* 2003). As the previous section has argued, however, this may not always be the case and for some young men becoming a father may have positive outcomes for them, their partner and child. For young people, however, early parenthood can bring a clash between teenage and adult discourses. Whilst I have considered young men in this chapter who have positioned their overall narratives progressively, arguing that their lives have generally improved, having moved from recklessness to responsibility, they also describe some of the difficulties of becoming a young father, and how different it is from being a teenager without responsibilities.

- **Too many responsibilities:** John summarises this feeling. 'I wish sometimes I was still, do you know what I mean, a kid, because I'm only seventeen. I can't do the things I want to do like go out every day, play football with my mates and having a few beers or something. Instead I've got to stop my baby from crying and clean the nappies.'

# Inter-professional approaches to young fathers

- **The tensions between the expectations of adolescence and adulthood** are also apparent for John. Although previously John described his girlfriend as saving him from his teenage addiction to drink, he admits that he is still tempted by a youthful identity and its association with freedom. Also of importance are the distrust and tensions within adolescent relationships (Hudson & Ineichen 1991). Talking about his partner John explains: 'It's just because like it's mucked up my life. I can't go out and do what I want when I want like a normal person my age that ain't got a kid. Like say if I wanted to go out clubbing then, I don't want to go out on my own because she gets paranoid about me and I get paranoid about her, so we would rather go out together and we can't for obvious reasons. Not even if we wanted to go out and see a film at the cinema, babies are not allowed in the cinema, are they?'

- Hudson and Ineichen (1991) point out that young relationships are fraught with tensions even without the added responsibility of parenthood. As John suggests, the parameters of trust in a relationship have to be negotiated, with young people navigating being a 'couple' as well as being new parents. As Gavin *et al.* point out, the quality of the relationship between a father and mother is a significant 'determinant of paternal involvement' (Gavin *et al.* 2002: 10). The authors argue that continued romantic investment between couples encourages the ongoing participation of the father with positive outcomes for the long-term development of the child. Understanding the causes of stress and tension from the perspective of the young father can aid professional intervention.

## Case transcript

### Keeping everyone happy

Manuel admits how hard he finds it to keep both his wife and children happy. I ask him how he finds being a father and a partner:

*Manuel:* Very difficult. Trying to keep everybody happy is very difficult. Spend too much time with the kids and then Kelly will get jealous, spend too much time with Kelly and the kids will get jealous. I find it very difficult to mix with both, if you know what I mean

# Recklessness, rescue and responsibility

> *Interviewer:* So how do you deal with it? How do you sort it out?
>
> *Manuel:* When we first had the children I wasn't very aware of it at all. Me and Kelly had some really big arguments about it. It was all Kelly or the kids. But as time goes on you kind of grow up and realise that you need to spend a certain amount of time with each other and try and share the time that you have got. I am better in the morning with the kids and then when they go to school it allows me and Kelly to do what she wants to do.

● Daniel draws attention to the subtle ongoing pressure he feels he has from his peers, who are not fathers, to join in with their activities: 'They all take the mickey out of me saying I'm "under the thumb" and I can't go out and all that, but there ain't no point going out when you've got responsibilities, you can't go out can you?'

A key feature of Daniel's current position is the way he has turned a negative representation by his friends that he is under the control of a woman, into a positive representation of himself and Sally as a couple. The implication is that he has moved on in his social activities as a couple rather than as a single man, a step associated with long-term positive implications for keeping out of trouble (Laub & Sampson 2003).

**Table 7.3**      **Positive outcomes of becoming a young father**

| Individual characteristics | Family features | Impact on the community |
|---|---|---|
| May give up crime and ASB<br><br>Becomes part of an intimate relationship<br><br>Participates in caring for a child<br><br>Thinks of the impact his own behaviour has on others – primarily his partner and child | Increases potential for social capital through formation of wider family networks<br><br>May be involved in the care of his child/children | Expresses desire to become a breadwinner and to gain employment<br><br>Impact of less ASB on community<br><br>Expresses concern at going back to prison/ youth custody |

## Conclusions and implications for practice

Desisting and withdrawing from crime and criminal relationships is a complex and lengthy process, with many zigzagging their way through it (Burnett 2004) and sometimes individuals are bound to crime by serious and ongoing financial or accommodation problems (Burnett & Maruna 2004). For young men there may also be pressures to conform from peers. However, having a child seems to be a strong motivating factor encouraging a positive change in behaviour. This point is significant in the light of much literature on young parents which highlights that having a child is a negative and socially excluding experience for the majority (SEU 1999, Swann *et al.* 2003).

Some young fathers referred to in this chapter explain that the circumstances of the pregnancy and birth of their child changed their perspective towards their peer group and this group no longer held the same importance. Consequently, behaviour and identities were described as being re-fashioned. Significant events and significant people, particularly meeting their current partner and either the prospect of or actually becoming a young father, were described as affecting their transition experience from one associated with recklessness to one embracing respon-sibility. As Thomson *et al.* (2002) maintain, 'critical moments' can change the route of a transition experience. For some young men the birth of their child is described positively, allowing them the opportunity to distance themselves from previous, antisocial behaviour and embrace responsibility. In places, however, their narratives are tempered with the challenges and tensions that being a teenager, young man and young father can bring. On the basis of these findings I would argue that professional attention needs to harness the positive, if difficult, renegotiations depicted by some young men during the transition to fatherhood as there are points during the process when they may need help, for example, in moving their lives on and distancing themselves from previous anti-social behaviour and influences, as well as helping them negotiate their identities as fathers. Professional focus, therefore, needs to be on both the young father and the young mother during the transition to parenthood, as they are both part of the equation and may both need help adjusting to their future roles.

**Figure 7.1**  **Key points for professional interventions with young fathers**

| | |
|---|---|
| Young man may need help with employment – provider role – or help with parenthood – carer role or distancing from previous networks | **Young man may need help from Connexions, Sure Start and Children's Centres as well as health visitors** |

↑

| | |
|---|---|
| Pregnancy as a result of poor sexual health practices or desire to become a father | **Engagement of young men by antenatal services and hospital midwives at birth** |

↑

| | |
|---|---|
| Young man sexually active | **Sexual health services and school nurses should be approachable and responsive** |

↑

| | |
|---|---|
| Young offender, peer pressure, poor educational achievements, living with social exclusion | **Professional interventions through YOT or social services** |

There are key times and key professionals who need to be alert to the needs of young men if their opportunities to develop as responsible fathers are to be maximised, in line with key contemporary policy and legislation and to ensure the positive long-term development of their child or children (DfES 2004).

## References

Billig, M., Condor, S., Edwards, D., Gane, M., Middleton, D. & Radley, A. (1988). *Ideological Dilemmas*. London: Sage Publications.

Burnett, R. (2000). 'Understanding criminal careers through a series of in-depth interviews' in *Offender Programme Report* 4(1): 14–16.

Burnett, R. (2004). 'To reoffend or not to reoffend? The ambivalence of convicted property offenders' in Maruna, S. & Immarigeon, R. (eds.) *After Crime and Punishment: Pathways to Offender Reintegration*. Cullompton: Willan.

Burnett, R. & Maruna, S. (2004). 'So "prison works", does it? The criminal careers of 130 men released from prison under Home Secretary, Michael Howard' in *The Howard Journal of Criminal Justice* 43(4): 390–404.

Coleman, J & Hendry, L. (2004). *The Nature of Adolescence*. London: Routledge.

Connell, R. (1995). *Masculinities*. Cambridge: Polity Press.

Connell, R.W. (2000). *The Men and the Boys*. Oxford: Polity Press.

Dennison, C. & Coleman, J. (2000). *Young People and Gender: A Review of Research*. Women's Unit, Cabinet Office & Family Policy Unit, The Home Office. London: HMSO.

Denzin, N.K. (1989). *Interpretative Biography: Qualitative Research Methods*. Series 17. London: Sage Publications

Department for Education and Skills (DfES) (2004). *Every Child Matters: Change for Children in Social Care*. London: The Stationery Office.

Frosh, S., Phoenix, A. & Pattman, R. (2002). *Young Masculinities*. Basingstoke: Palgrave.

Frost, L. (2001). *Young Women and the Body: A Feminist Sociology*. Basingstoke: Palgrave.

Gavin, L.E., Black, M. M., Minor, S., Abel, Y., Papas, M. & Bentley, M. (2002). 'Young, disadvantaged fathers' involvement with their infants: An ecological perspective' in *Journal of Adolescent Health* 31(3): 266–276.

Giddens, A. (1991). *Modernity and Self Identity: Self and Society in the Late Modern Age*. Cambridge: Polity.

Graham, J. & Bowling, B. (1995). *Young People and Crime* (Home Office Research Study No. 145). London: Home Office.

Henderson et al (2007)

Henderson C.E., Young, D.W., Jainchill,N., Hawke, J., Farkas, S., Meghan Davis, R.(2007). 'Programme use of effective drug abuse treatment practices for juvenile offenders.' *Journal of Substance Abuse Treatment* 32 (3): 279-290

Hudson, F. & Ineichen, B. (1991). *Taking it Lying Down: Sexuality and Teenage Motherhood*. Basingstoke: Macmillan Publishing.

Johnston, L., MacDonald, R., Mason, P., Ridley, L. & Webster, C. (2000). 'The impact of social exclusion on young people moving into adulthood.' Available online at: www.jrf.org.uk/knowledge/findings/socialpolicy/030 (accessed 2002).

Jones, G. (2003). *The Youth Divide: Diverging Paths to Adulthood*. York: Joseph Rowntree Foundation. Available online at: www.jrf.org.uk/knowledge/findings/socialpolicy (accessed 2002).

Kiernan, K. (1995). 'The transition to parenthood: Young mothers, young fathers, associated factors and later life experiences.' Discussion Paper 113, London, LSE.

Laub, J.H. & Sampson, R.J. (2003). *Shared Beginings, Divergent Lives*. Cambridge MA: Harvard University Press.

Lloyd, T. & Forrest, S. (2001). 'Boys and young men's health: Literature and practice review.' Health Development Agency. Available online at: www.hda-online.org.uk/documents/boyshealth (accessed 2003).

Mandelbaum, D.G. (1973). 'The study of life history: Gandhi' in *Current Anthropology* 14: 177–196.

Maruna, S. (2000). 'Desistance from crime and offender rehabilitation: A tale of two research literatures' in *Offender Programs Report* 4: 1–13.

McDowell, L. (2001). 'Young men's views of masculinity'. Available at: www.jrf.org.uk/knowledge/findings/socialpolicy/421

McQueen, C. & Henwood, K. (2002). 'Young men in crisis: Attending to the language of teenage boys' distress' in *Social Science and Medicine* 55: 1493–1509.

Oakely, A. (1979). *Becoming a Mother*. Oxford: Martin Robinson.

Quieniart, S. (2004). 'A profile of fatherhood among young men: Moving away from their birth family and closer to their child' in *Sociological Research Online* 9(3).

Raffo, C. & Reeves, M. (2000). 'Youth transitions and social exclusion: developments in social capital theory' in *Journal of Youth Studies* 3(2): 147–166.

Reeves, J. (2006). *'You've got to keep your head on' A study of the stories young male service users tell about the transition to fatherhood*. Unpublished thesis: The Open University.

Social Exclusion Unit (1999). *Teenage Pregnancy*. London: HMSO.

Social Exclusion Unit (2004). *Impact of the Teenage Pregnancy Strategy: Programme Report*. London: HMSO. Available online at: www.dfes.gov.uk/teenagepregnancy (accessed 2005).

Stephen, D.E. & Squires, P.A. (2003). 'Adults don't realise how sheltered they are. A contribution to the debate on youth transitions from some voices on the margins' in *Journal of Youth Studies* 6(2): 145–164.

Swann, C., Bowe, K., McCormic, G. & Kosmin, M. (2003). *Teenage Pregnancy and Parenthood: A Review of Reviews: Evidence Briefing*. www.hda.nhs.uk (accessed 2004).

Thomson, R. & Holland, J. (1998). 'Sexual relationships, negotiation and decision making' in Coleman, J.& Roker, D. (eds) *Teenage Sexuality: Health, Risk and Education*. London: Harwood Academic Publishers.

Thomson, R., Bell, R., Holland, J., Henderson, S, McGrellis, S. & Sharpe, S. (2002). 'Critical moments: Choice, chance and the opportunity in young people's narratives of transition' in *Sociology* 36(2): 335–354.

Tyrer, P., Chase, E., Warwick, I. & Aggleton, P. (2005). '"Dealing with it." Experiences of young fathers in and leaving care' in *British Journal of Social Work* 35: 1107–1121.

Unruh, D., Bullis, M. & Yovanoff, P. (2003). 'Community reintegration outcomes for formerly incarcerated adolescent fathers and non fathers' in *Journal of Emotional and Behavioural Disorders* 1: 144–156.

Webster, C., Simpson, M. (2006) 'Predicting Criminality? Risk Factors, Neighbourhood Influence and Desistance.' *Youth Justice* 6(1): 7–22.

Welch, M., Price, E.A., Yankey, N.(2002) 'Moral Panic Over Youth Violence.' *Youth and Society* 34(1) 3–30

Wellings, K., Field, J., Johnson, A. & Wadsworth, J. (1994). *Sexual Behaviour in Britain*. London: Penguin.

Wellings, K. & Mitchell, K. (1998). 'Risks associated with early sexual activity and fertility' in Roker, D. & Coleman, J. (eds.) *Teenage Sexuality: Health, Risk and Education*. London: Harwood Academic.

Wellings, K., Nanchahal, K., MacDowell, W., McManus, S. & Erens, R. (2001). 'Sexual health in Britain: Early heterosexual experiences' in *Lancet* 358: 1843–1850.

Whyte, B. 'Effectiveness, Research and Youth Justice.' *Youth Justice* 4(1) 3–21.

# Index